Somewhere in Germany

Based on a True Story

Deborah G. King

KING PUBLICATIONS
DALTON, GEORGIA

Cover art: Deborah G. King
Book design/Cover layout: Steffi Rubin

ISBN 978-0-615-16426-7
Printed in the U.S.A.

Dedication

To my beloved husband David, the love of my life,
who has always stood beside me through good times and bad.

For my children who are the heart of my soul,
for my families, Harris, King, and Crook.

For Mark Pace, editor, who inspires me, because at
91 years of age he still writes for the Dalton newspaper.

Special Thanks to

Marie and Ignaz Ackermann
for encouragement and insight.

Ava Wyatt, German teacher,
for insight into German culture.

Vera Nagel of Frankfurt, Germany
for her help in Germany.

The many others who helped and inspired,
and had faith that I could write this book.

Contents

Chapter 1	The Beginning	1
Chapter 2	Tails Creek	7
Chapter 3	The War	11
Chapter 4	The Road to Appenrode	15
Chapter 5	Somewhere in Germany	25
Chapter 6	Fahrenzhausen	37
Chapter 7	The Beginning of Fall in Fahrenzhausen	57
Chapter 8	A Dangerous Mission	65
Chapter 9	Christmas in Germany	75
Chapter 10	The Unexpected Departure	85
Chapter 11	Back to Ramhurst in the After Math of War	91
Chapter 12	Letters from Anna	99
Chapter 13	The Later Years	109
Chapter 14	The Farm	113
Chapter 15	The Letters	121
Chapter 16	Love Knows No Boundaries	129
Chapter 17	Truth Will Stand When the World Falls Down	139
Chapter 18	The Shock of It All	149
Chapter 19	The Family Comes Full Circle	155
Chapter 20	Letters from Germany, Modern Day	159
The Ending		169

1
The Beginning

*W*e had spent days at County Hospital, watching and waiting for a word of encouragement from the doctors. They all just kept shaking their heads, saying there wasn't much hope. We needed to accept this.

We had all begged Paul to fight for his life because we were afraid that his condition was worsening by the hour and that he would eventually slip away. We could not accept what the doctors told us. Paul had been such a strong figure in our lives we couldn't imagine life without him.

"You have to do something—anything—to save him!" Charles broke down and cried as he urged the doctor to please do something more.

"His kidneys are beginning to fail," the doctor explained. "Among all his other problems, his kidneys are only functioning at about seventeen percent." Charles kept begging the doctor not to let the brother he had known and lived with for seventy-five years…not to let him die.

The doctor looked resistant but finally said, "The only hope is to transfer him to Dalton and put him on dialysis. Then there's a slim chance that Dr. Langley can help him." Dr. Park bent her head; she knew there wasn't really much of a chance and her heart felt heavy also, for she had known Paul for years and knew that Charles and Mary needed their brother.

"Then let's do it." Charles answered, hope flickering in his eyes. "If we can get him over there and his kidneys begin to function better then maybe he could pull out of this. I hope we haven't waited too long."

Dr. Park put the orders in for the transfer to the Dalton hospital, the only large hospital within a 25-mile radius. County Hospital was a small community hospital and more serious illnesses and surgeries were always sent to Dalton.

Paul Crook had other problems as well that had sent him to the hospital in the first place. In the 1980s, Paul's lungs had been afflicted with pneumonia and bronchitis. He had been on oxygen because of a stroke in 1986; the doctors did not give him much time to live then either. The doctors said it would take a drastic change in Paul's condition to pull him through and to overcome his illness. Charles had taken great care of Paul during those stressful days almost twenty years earlier. Now it was 2001. We knew Charles had done a good job making Paul take care of himself, enforcing a certain diet and helping him to quit smoking.

Charles had lived with Paul for at least seventy years and he was not about to give up on his brother now either. Paul's wheezing spells started on Tuesday night after a bad cold. Charles called an ambulance to take Paul to the hospital.

At Dalton Hospital, Paul was sent to intensive care. We could only see him once every two hours. They hooked him up to the dialysis machine and this took a while because of the trip from Chatsworth to Dalton. Dr. Langley, a kidney specialist in Dalton worked on Paul in the intensive care unit. They decided to let us see him as soon as they got Paul hooked up to the dialysis and the ventilator which help him to breathe. He had already been on life-support for a few days.

Mary, Paul's only living sister (and my mother-in-law) walked beside me into intensive care. I wanted to be strong for her because she felt the same way that Charles did: she wasn't ready to let go—not if there was a chance. As we stood by Paul's bedside, it was almost as difficult for me as it was for her. Seeing him hooked up to all the wires and tubes that were going in and out of his body was hard. The shock of seeing a once-vibrant life now in this state was almost unbearable. I focused on the tubes with the blood in it, circulating his blood from the dialysis machine back into his body.

Dr. Langley came in and spoke to Mary.

"He should start improving soon," he told her. Mary stood there, touching Paul on the arm with tears in her eyes.

"Paul", she said to him, "maybe this will make you feel better. You just hang on and let the machine do what it's supposed to, and maybe you will get better." Mary did not want to leave him but our ten minutes were up and someone else would be allowed in.

They say that just before you die your life flashes before you; scenes and conversations run through your mind. As we looked down at him that night in the hospital, Paul was already starting to leave us. His mind was urging him to fight, as Charles had said, but he was drawn into that other world where he could see Anna as she ran down the street before him. He could see her smile and toss her hair as she looked back at him. He wanted to go to her...follow her. There, too, was his mother, so happy to welcome him home from the war, relieved that he hadn't been killed like so many others. That final battle was going on inside him. Paul struggled to stay, but the warmth of beckoning feelings overcame him, and eventually he succumbed.

Paul died about twenty minutes after the family's final visit. We had all had hopes that he could have come out of the kidney failure, but Dr. Langley said, even with life support that when you die, you just die.

I'm sure I flunked history in high school but for some reason, I became interested into it later in life. My Grandfather died in 1982 and it was then that I became a historical researcher and genealogy buff. Family history is as addictive to me as drugs are to others and I never could get enough of it. While looking for my own family history, I accidentally came across the Crook family history from Samuel Tate, in the late 1700s to now. This information was dumped in my lap quite by accident—a gift from a distant cousin.

At Paul's funeral it was important to me to hear conversations from cousins and relatives that I had never met before. Many old family members had all already died. The two oldest remaining relatives were Mary and Charles, and it occurred to me then that although I knew quite a bit about the family's past, and even something about more current history I really did not know very much about Charles' and Mary's own stories. I decided to make this discovery a priority.

Paul was well thought of, a "kind and gentle man," everyone said. Quiet, but with a good sense of humor that he showed more around the family than strangers. He was a good person who would give you the shirt off of his back if he thought you needed it. He would speak about the war, having served in World War II; but what began as simple truthful detail would suddenly take a turn and become some cockamamie story! Soon you couldn't tell if he was telling the truth or pulling your leg. His mischievous laugh made you wonder all the more. One that I particularly remember was something about a B-1 Bomber; every one knew he was in the Army as a foot soldier and not in the Air Force, so we all assumed this was one of his pranks.

Paul's mother Adell had donated land to the church the family attended, and you could see it from the old farm house where Charles, and Paul, and their mother, Adell Crook had lived. They still owned the land just next to the church and had started a graveyard for the family members next to the church on a high hill, overlooking the farm and all its acreage. There, a wind always seemed to blow a light breeze.

In this cemetery, we laid Paul to rest on that high hill, for to me, it was the most appropriate place for Paul to be buried. It was a place that Paul used to go and sit on a fallen tree, now rotted and decayed over time. He would come to this place, and think about Anna, when life seemed too overwhelming, when missing her was unbearable. There sitting on this tree he would escape to another place and time where he could see her and be with her, just as it was supposed to have been. His grave became the most prominent grave on the hill, just inside the fence that the family had erected to protect the sacred ground and family memories.

Somewhere in Germany

There, on Paul's grave, sits a marble tombstone with a farm and tractor on it. At the foot of the grave is a memorial to the service he did as a soldier in World War II, honoring him for his duty in the foreign service. It was hard for us to leave his grave site. We stood there for what seemed like the longest time. This was the finality of it all. Paul was gone. It was time that we were all going to have to face life without him.

2
Tails Creek

J recall my first trip to Tails Creek when I was younger. David and I had only been married for a short time so I know it was around 1977 or 1978 when he took me there. Just a spot on the road, a small community with a church appropriately called Tails Creek Baptist Church. Turn left just across from the church and it takes you up into the hollow where the Sanfords and Corbins live now. Around 1935, just after Jim Crook, the father of the family, died, the Crook family moved to Tails Creek from Chatsworth. They made the move so that Paul and Charles could farm, raising enough vegetables to take to Atlanta to the farmers' market where you could get a decent price from your surplus crops.

That was the only way a family could make a decent living here in the hollow. People in this area were poor and what you didn't put up in your root cellar or pantry went to profits for the family when they took it to market. Vegetables were the staple other than the yearly killing of hogs usually in the fall, when the meat was either smoked in a smoke house or salted and cured in a saltbox.

In that hollow stands a few old rickety looking homes; some would refer to them as shacks by today's standards, but during the early 1940s that was the best that anyone could do in that area. The depression years had passed, but this area was recovering very slowly.

The nearest industry could be found in Dalton where they manufactured bedspreads, but Tails Creek was far enough from Dalton to make it hard to earn a living. When the Crook family had lived in Ramhurst, they had tufted the bedspreads by hand with a big needle. Someone from the company would come bring the materials, and the family would do the labor; later, whoever had brought the materials, would return to pick up the finished product, pay the family for the labor and bring more materials. This is how they made their living. The finished product would then go to Dalton for sale at the bedspread outlets that would line Highway 41 in North Georgia, an area known then as Peacock Alley. People from the north driving south on Highway 41 (the only highway from the north to the south, all the way into Florida) would drive by the outlets, sometimes stopping to purchase one of the beautiful hand-sewn bedspreads.

When the family moved to Tails Creek, Paul and Charles were given the responsibility to make the gardens bigger and more prosperous so they would have plenty to take to market. This meant getting up early and working all day picking, doing their regular chores, and driving to the market later in the week to sell their goods. In the winter the brothers worked at a nearby saw mill, and when they had time, they would also pick cotton in the fall—all of it just to put food on the table. Other than trips to market, there was little time to get out of the hollow, and when they did it was a rare occasion, like a a church social, a funeral or a wedding. A rolling store would come by occasionally and they would trade what goods they could for things they needed for cooking and clothes making.

Tails Creek is a small community just west of Ellijay, and just east of Chatsworth. A mountainous community nestled far into the foothills of the Blue Ridge mountain range, folks in this hollow rented old houses better known as salt box houses. These were two-story houses that just went straight up with no front porch and was quite plain and of a simple design. This house was older and with thin walls and its own ghostly haunts.

Mrs. Adell Crook's oldest daughter by her first husband, Hilda and Hilda's husband, Cleve had originally settled here and their descendants still live and thrive here today. Mrs. Crook had met her husband Jim following the deaths of his first wife and her first husband. Each brought three children to the marriage; then Jim and his new wife had seven more over the next ten years before Jim died. Addie, Lea, and Juanita had all died young. The remaining children of this marriage were Paul, Charles, Mary and William.

Life at Tails Creek was good for several years but in the end, Mrs. Crook realized they needed to move back to Chatsworth, to be closer to the bedspread industry, so that work would be more readily available. They rented a house on the Old Ramhurst Road just south of the talc mine. They had no money to buy a home, because once Jim died, Adell only had enough money for the bare essentials. Today, the talc mine is just two really big holes in the ground where all the talc has been mined out of there. All the talc was blasted by dynamite during the '40s and '50s to make various products from the talc powder. Talc powder was also a popular filler in many products.

One day, the family was all at the house except Adell's oldest son Simon who worked at the mines, when news came from the mine that two men had been injured. A cave in the work area had given way. Panic grabbed Adell's heart and then suddenly sorrow when men came from the mine to say that Simon had been killed when a boulder fell on him and one other man. The other man was badly injured but Simon had died shortly after being crushed.

Adell's life had been already been turbulent, losing two husbands, three children when they were young—and now Simon who had lived to be a young adult. He had always been thoughtful of the other children and the younger ones were crushed at losing Simon whom they looked up to as a father figure.

The burden of the family fell upon Adell's oldest son living at home then. Paul shouldered the responsibilities of father and older brother and, even at the age of fourteen, assumed the task of providing for the younger children and making sure the family had something to eat at suppertime.

3
The War

*A*lthough World War II was being fought, in Chatsworth, you would never know that America was at war. Except for rumors that someone had been drafted, or someone's loved one was returning home, newspapers were scarce and word of mouth did not keep up with the details of the war down the mountain and across the sea.

One day news came from the Department of the Army that Paul Earl Crook was being called to duty. He had just turned eighteen and was told to report to boot camp. It was 1944 and although the worst of World War II was over, fighting continued.

Adell had seen so much tragedy in her life, she could not accept the fact that her young son was going to have to go to the Army. In the back of everyone's mind was the fear that Paul could be sent to Germany though no one was saying it; no one wanted to imagine that he would have to go to war.

Paul awoke the morning he was to leave and performed his usual chores just as if nothing was amiss, as though the day was a day like any other; but today it was very different. Paul, who had assumed the role of the father figure after Simon died, would be leaving his home today for the United States Army. Finally, it was time to catch the bus that would be taking him for his basic training at Fort Bragg, North Carolina. He took his bags and set them by the front door. The younger of the children and Adell, his mother all gathered around to say goodbye. The younger children cried and held him as long as they could, and then Adell had to say goodbye again to one of her children.

"Don't worry mother." Paul said. "I'll be fine, and I will write you as much as possible, to let you know that I am O.K."

"You just be O.K., son." She replied with tears in her eyes.

Mary told me that they watched him go; that they watched the bus leave, driving down the road. She said it was one of the hardest days of her life.

Paul trained in boot camp for six weeks and wrote to his mother several times during his training. As soon as he began to receive a salary, he had arranged for his mother to receive most of his military pay. He only hoped it would be enough. He feared that without his help on the farm and the extra money he and Charles made, the family might go hungry.

Paul then went to Fort Hood, Texas where he excelled in marksmanship. Being the bashful, quiet man that he was and not really knowing any of the men in his unit, Paul put his energy into being the best that he could be, and he was good. He began ironing the other soldiers clothing to make extra money, because it was a job no one wanted; but Paul saw the extra money as a way to help his family. Months later, when there was talk of going to Germany, Paul did not know how to tell his mother.

Paul first traveled to New York; from there he headed out overseas. He wrote and told his mother that he had to go and fight in the war. When she got the letter, she cried and prayed to God to watch over him—wherever he had to go.

4
The Road
to Appenrode

*P*aul left New York on February 17, 1945, and arrived in Central Europe a couple of weeks after that. His military papers do not state where he was sent first, but his unit was placed in a stable area until they started to move about Germany. They went from town to town, usually just after a battle and just after the town was captured by the allied forces. They had not seen hand-to-hand combat. They camped at night around areas where there were other units also camped and they heard stories about the battles they had been involved in.

Paul's unit would arrive to find another unit had already built camp, got a camp fire going, and had pitched a mess tent where they would be cooking grub. The men would all sit around the campfire after eating and swapping stories. This was how Paul got to know some of the other men in his unit. Most of the men were from the south, but there was one from New Jersey (appropriately nicknamed "New Jersey"), and one from Arizona. These soldiers had all been together since Fort Hood, Texas.

It was a cold winter, and they had marched through snow and mud. A fresh snow would fall again and the mud would freeze underneath it. You could see traces where another army unit had been, whether it was German or American; when they saw tracks, they would be on alert and on the defensive in case they ran into the enemy. Sometimes when the tracks looked fresh, they would change course to avoid incident.

The bitter cold was brutal; wind and snow blew to the point that sometimes they had to look for an old abandoned farmhouse or barn just to get out of the weather. A bed of hay in a barn was preferable to braving the fierce elements of winter. They would play cards in the daylight when camped and some of the men would gamble...but not Paul. He would never risk any of his money on such a trivial thing. At late evening, all fires had to go out and no light could come from any of the cracks in the barn wall, for it could give up their location to the enemy and could invite an attack on amongst themselves. Sometimes it would get dark about four or five o'clock in the evening. They would rise early and be on their way before daybreak.

It was a hard life, hard on the body because of the continuous walking that caused foot sores from wet socks and boots. And, of course, they would not have a bath for weeks.

Little did he realize, Private Crook's life would be forever changed on the morning of March 18, 1945. That morning was clear but cold, and although there were times when it was so cold at night, that the soldiers would dig holes and crawl into them just to keep from freezing to death. This morning, it was a bit warmer as they marched down the road toward the small town of Appenrode, Germany. Gear strapped to their backs and rifles hung over their shoulders, they marched for what seemed to be an eternity. Breaking camp before daybreak, they suddenly found themselves involved in an attack. Peaceful and quiet one moment, the air exploded with noise the next moment.

The sudden rata-tat-tat of guns firing in the distance took the unit by surprise. Paul and one of his friends had just been having a conversation when Paul turned to look back at him to answer a question and his friend went down, hit by a round of fire.

All the men scrambled for cover on the bank on the opposite side of the dirt road, but the bullets kept coming heavily and before some of the men could even unload their packs off their backs, they were struck by the enemy gunfire and killed.

Paul crawled down the bank to get out of the firestorm of bullets that rained down upon them and he yelled his friend's name. He unloaded his gear off his back, grabbed his rifle and started back up the bank. Some of the men began to fire back after they realized which direction the gunfire was coming from.

"John!" Paul called. "John!" he screamed again as he tried to access what was going on in the woods across the road. There he could see German soldiers hiding behind trees guarded by a metal shield on a piece of military equipment.

Paul wanted to help John, but the gunfire was coming much heavier. Paul then saw the side of John's head: a massive amount of blood coming out of a hole just below his helmet. If he wasn't dead, he would be in a matter of minutes.

Paul crawled back to a more guarded area, looked around and realized that every one of the other men around him had been hit in the initial surprise attack. Some were wounded, but most had been killed.

Paul lay still in that safe area, until he saw the Germans starting to come out of the woods, towards them. All the gunfire had stopped and the Germans probably assumed that they had killed all the men in Paul's unit.

They got nearer and nearer until Paul could hear them talking to each other in German. None of the other men in his unit was firing, so it was up to him. Still, he waited until they were all out of the woods and visibly close. He began firing until he plowed the first and second row of the men down. He continued to shoot, thinking of the dead that lay around him. This moment would be for John and the others. There was no stopping him and his gun. He grabbed a couple of rifles next to him that had belonged to the dead men around him and kept firing.

Eventually he noticed the arms of the Germans going up in surrender. He got on his knees and up onto his feet. He was so angry, he gritted his teeth, felt down to see if John was breathing, but John was gone, which made Paul even more angry.

"I should kill you all, you stupid bastards!" he screamed as he ran toward them holding the rifle securely until he reached the place where the Germans were standing with their hands up. He held the gun high aiming directly at the men who stood before him, and they all were trembling, muttering something in German.

Paul motioned them to move closer to the road, holding the gun on them the whole time. The men gathered into a bunch and Paul went and found a piece of long rope, and motioned for them to walk to the nearest tree. There he tied them around the tree and went to see if he could help any of the men in his unit. They were all dead except for one soldier named Robert who was shot in the shoulder and had lost quite a bit of blood. Paul stuffed a handkerchief in the guy's heavy wool uniform and told him to lay there till, hopefully, the bleeding would stop.

"Just lay there. I'll be back in a few minutes," he told Robert, all the while looking back at his captives tied to the tree. None of them was moving as they leaned against each other.

Paul then ran across the road and examined the dead Germans. "Oh my God," he thought. There were a lot of men laying there lifeless. He had killed these men during his extreme rage.

Suddenly one of the Germans broke loose and started towards a rifle lying near the dead soldiers.

Paul shot him in the head, and the soldier stumbled to the ground. The other German soldiers that were tied scuffled around with fear. They decided that they were better off alive and doing what the American said, than to die as their comrade just had. They were in total surrender.

Several times that day, Paul checked on Robert. The wounded man sit up once, until he felt weak and then lay back down. Paul got his friend some water and he managed a sip or two. He had felt of all the men's pulses just to make sure they were all dead, and they were, everyone except him and Robert.

Paul felt overwhelmed and wanted to cry, but he had to be strong. He could hear the Germans having a conversation amongst themselves in a language that he could not understand. But he did not care at this point. He was still stunned that this had all happened, and now he had 24 men captured and tied to a tree, one of them injured slightly and a comrade of his own unit who was more seriously injured. He was more concerned about Robert and did not care if the Germans were comfortable or not.

Night began to fall. Paul covered Robert up with blankets out of the dead men's gear, hoping that he would not get hypothermia from lying on the cold ground. He gave the Germans nothing but a sip of water just before dark. He had to stay nearer to the Germans than to Robert because there were so many of them and they could try to escape or gang up on him if they could get their hands freed. But they had not resisted, although they kept muttering something in German to each other.

"Amerikaner," one said, "Amerikaner," with his German accent. Paul looked at him as he was leaning at the tree near them. The German tried to motion that they were hungry but Paul just muttered "nein," which he knew meant "no" in German. He had no interest in making the Germans comfortable after they had butchered all the men in his unit. Paul had been so enraged at the time of their capture that he could easily have killed them all, and though it was his responsibility to keep them, try to do something for them? No he would not!

Paul's mother had taught her children right from wrong and Paul was now dealing with the fact that killing was wrong and against God. "What would my mother think of me now?" he wondered, sitting amongst the dead he had befallen earlier in the day.

Adell. He had not thought of his mother and his life back in Georgia that whole, horrible day. How far he was from home, and the life he had always known. Tears came to his eyes and this time it was O.K. It was dark and no one was going to see his tears.

In the morning Paul awoke to the rumble of a truck in the distance. He had mostly been awake all night but had dozed off for a moment, just before day break. He was surprised that the Germans had not taken advantage of his nap, but realized as he looked over, that they too, were all asleep. The nightmare of the previous day's events hit him again and he got up to check on Robert. Robert was still alive, and doing fair. Paul told him to hang on, that he could see a truck coming and it was American.

The American army truck came and when the drivers saw what Paul had done, they exclaimed how excellent a job Paul had done holding the German soldiers captive until they arrived. Paul was more concerned about getting Robert to the hospital than anything, and told them to please hurry him to a place where they could get him some help. Robert was the only surviving member of Paul's unit besides him, and the battle had raged in his head all night, as he had relived the events of the day before, and the awfulness of what had happened in the shooting.

They loaded the German captives, and placed Robert in the cab of the truck along with the two military men who had come in the truck. They would see that Robert was taken to a medic immediately and they would send another truck to pick up the dead. They offered Paul a ride back, but he refused, and said that he wanted to stay there until another truck came, out of respect for his dead and fallen comrades.

When the truck pulled away, and drove out of sight, Paul walked over to the German dead. There he looked amongst the bodies, and realized that when it came down to it, that people was just people. He had killed these men, and he asked God to forgive him. If it weren't for these dead, he would probably be laying among the dead across the road with the American bodies. He knew that he should go over to the other side of the road, and look at the bodies of his friends, but it was so very hard to think about them being gone, when yesterday morning, they had all had breakfast together.

Paul made himself face them, as he walked across, and encountered the dead bodies that lay before him. He immediately started to sob, as he repositioned the dead not to look like they had after they were killed—like rag dolls flung here and there. He thought about how some of them had told tales of back home and their loved ones, and how now they would never see them again. How sad, to die in a far off country, Paul thought, and wondered if their bodies would be sent back to the states or would they be buried in this God-forsaken land?

"I'm sorry!" he yelled, in the quietness of the countryside as he looked up to the sky.

"I'm so sorry." Paul broke out in another round of sadness and tears. "New Jersey" lay face down. Paul turned him over, and looked at his face. He could see his buddy looked peaceful now, but had died with a bullet wound to the lung area. The pain was probably very intense and Paul imagined that it must have been agony just before the life had left his body.

When the next truck came, to retrieve the bodies, Paul was no where to be found. He had walked off into the woods, had to be alone, for he had so much sorrow and so much that he had to happen to him that he just wanted to be by himself for awhile. One of the drivers from that truck came looking for him, and when he saw him, he knew exactly why Paul had wanted to be alone. This war was heck and if it didn't affect you, then you were not human. He talked to Paul about how he understood what he was going through and told him that the best thing he could do was to let it all out, and then have some counseling with the chaplain. Paul would just hold it inside. It would forever affect his life, he knew. You don't experience something like this and go on as though nothing ever happened. He hoped and prayed that nothing like this could come his way again; he walked from the woods, climbed up into the truck and was quiet the whole way back to camp.

5
Somewhere
in Germany

"What you did back there on the road to Appenrode was tremendous, very courageous and beyond the call of duty, Crook. I am going to see to it that you get a medal," Commander Lewis said to Paul as he sat in his tent after a debriefing of the battle of Appenrode.

"I don't care about any medal." Paul replied, he looked solemn and was tired of thinking about the killings he had had to do.

The Commander picked up on Paul's attitude. "Now Crook, war is war and if we have to do things that affect us, then we just have to do it. Before long all this will just be a memory. I am reassigning you to a new unit. We have taken München and there's a big area that we have to guard the borders of, so I will be sending you to join a unit north of München. When Robert has recuperated he will be joining you there. Your new Commander's name is Bridges."

Paul joined his new unit two days later. There was a lot of traveling; this area seemed very far away from where he had been before. No fighting here it seemed, except for the ruins from the bombing he noticed as the truck passed the little villages and towns. A truck loaded with soldiers and gear drove around for days delivering men, tents, and equipment that they would need to stand post. Paul and four other men were dropped off at a three way intersection on a dirt road. There was nothing here except dirt and trees and a small town just below them. They would have to set up camp from scratch. They pitched the huge tent and scrambled around to put everything in its place. This was all started by the early hours of dawn, and now it was late afternoon. They still had to dig a hole for the latrine and put a canvas shield over all the way around. It was near the woods way behind the tent.

Evening came and the smell of food wafting from the make-shift kitchen was very appealing. This would be the first real food he would have all day. The unit had designated a cook who had put together a stew and all the men eagerly ate it up. They agreed that the man chosen had certainly been the best choice for cook. They all slept fitfully that night with one of them staying awake in shifts in case some enemy soldiers decided to try to attack. There was no real noise out here except the spring crickets beginning to chirp. The town lights below had gone out long ago. No one wanted to burn oil uselessly because everything was scarce during the war.

The next day they had plenty of work to do. They had been instructed to clear any bushes or brush off the sides of the intersection and there was quite a bit of brush. They had to dig two holes, one on one side of the road and one straight across from it on the other side for the poles to hold the stop gate. When they heard a truck come rumbling down from the hill towards the town, the men grabbed their guns, startled. It was their job to stop the truck to search it for any hidden weapons, soldiers or contraband. If everything checked out, the driver had to state where he was headed and then the guard would decide to let him pass and go on ahead or whether to detain him for further inspection. This truck was of no threat and trying to communicate with the driver was quite difficult. One of the other men in Paul's unit spoke just enough German to understand the driver's intentions. So they waved him thru and went back to the other task at hand. An American truck came late in the day, just before dark and delivered more equipment and supplies for more work for the next few days. As darkness drew, the sun went down on the little town below and a few dim lights were all that remained. But not for long, they too went dark before long.

Late that night, Private Crook wrote his mother a letter by candlelight. It was the first letter he had written in over a week. He always put "Somewhere in Germany" in the corner of every letter and the date. All his letters seemed to say the same things. They were ordered by the military not to divulge any information in their letters. He couldn't tell her anything about where he was or anything about what he was doing, so he wrote, just to let her know that he was O.K. and when she received them she knew that he had survived awhile longer and hadn't been killed.

The third day was more work, the truck that had brought them more equipment had given them new jobs to do. They drilled post and filled the holes they had dug out the previous day. They created a barrier with poles that crossed in the middle to give the appearance to any vehicle that they were to stop.

Suddenly the men brought their heads up to notice three old men walking up the hill from the little town below. They held up their arms as if to surrender and walked towards the soldiers. They spoke in German when they were near the Americans. Guns were ready to be drawn if needed.

"Was machen sie hir?" One of the German said loudly. Private Dailey, the one who could speak a little German listened intently to what the men were saying. "I think they want to know why we are here and what we are doing?, Dailey told the rest of the unit. He tried to explain with some words and gestures that they would be guarding the road as a border patrol.

The old men eased a bit, relaxing their arms and hanging them back by their sides.

"Nur alte Manner, Frauen und Kinder wohnen jetzt heir." One German said to Dailey. Dailey explained that he was saying, "only old men, women, and children were living in the town now."

"Kein Krieg" the man continued. Which meant "No war. Please." He also told the unit, that of the young men who had lived there, that they had joined the German army and had either been killed or not heard from since. He said they only wanted the war to stop, and wasn't ones to want to cause problems to the American men. As they went back down the road to the town, they waved goodbye to the American soldiers and smiled to show that they were friendly.

When the post was complete, the men built a little shack-like building beside the road into München. It was a little-traveled road considering the trucks and cars that had come their way. The men at this stop took 4-hour turns standing guard, and they stood guard twice a day, usually once in the morning and then later in the evening or at night. The hours that passed in the shack were quite boring with only an overturned bucket to sit on. Occasionally a car or truck would come by carrying supplies in or out of München. Vegetables came from the garden district, and this little town was in the garden district. You could see the farmers in their gardens down the hill into the valley. It made Paul think about him and Charles farming back in Tails Creek. Paul felt like he had been in this one spot for a month or more, and he had watched people in the small town come and go, children playing in the streets with a ball, and watched old ladies hang out their laundry to dry.

On this particular day, he noticed a little girl peering at him from behind a fence post. She was quite far from him as he sat in the guard shack, but her stare made him notice that she was watching him. She had pretty blonde hair, and brown eyes, and her hair was in pigtails and pulled across the top of her head like a headband. Paul waved his hand at her to say hello, but she laughed softly and ran back down towards the town. It made him smile that she had been watching him.

A few days later, he had dragged the bucket seat just outside the little guard shack. Paul was basking in the spring sunshine, after the cold winter; the warm sun felt so good. He couldn't help but notice how blue the sky was and how big and white the clouds were up above. It had to be May by now but he wasn't sure because he'd had trouble keeping up with the days lately.

Again the little girl was peering again at him from the same fence post. He waved again, as he had a few days earlier and she smiled. But she did not run away this time. She slowly stuck her hand up and waved back. Paul smiled at her and she smiled back. Here he was in the midst of a war and this little girl, so sweet and innocent looking, was smiling at him. He silently said "thank you God" for such a simple pleasure. He reached into his pocket and pulled out a piece of gum wrapped in tin foil. He held it out toward her as a gesture of friendship. She eased slowly toward him and suddenly stopped a few feet from him. Looking down at the ground, she was apparently quite shy, so Paul extended his arm till the gum was right in front of her face. She grabbed it and smelled and unwrapped it hastily and stuck it into her mouth. She chewed it a minute, smiled and waved and ran back down the hill to the town.

On May 7th, 1945, the Germans signed papers of unconditional surrender, but the news of the war being over really didn't get to the troops till May 8th, 1945. Winston Churchill declared that day-V day for Victory.

The war was over and when the news reached Paul's unit, the men were excited. Maybe it wouldn't be long till they returned home and what a glad day that would be! The news came via a truck that was delivering supplies and the soldier driving the truck said he had seen such happiness all around the area.

"I have only been in Germany for six months and now we are going to get to go home." one of the guys said. "I figured I'd surely be here for at least a year or so. I guess we kicked those krauts' butts."

"You haven't seen any combat, Conway." Dailey said as he playfully smacked the younger guy upside the head. "You wouldn't know combat if you stepped right into it."

"Have you seen any combat, Crook?" Conway asked.

"Nothing to speak of," Paul replied. Even though he hated lying, he wasn't about to tell them about the battle of Appenrode.

Late in the day, some of the townspeople from the little town of Fahrenzhausen just below the post came up and wanted to know if the news that they had heard about the war being over was true. The American soldiers gladly told them that it was true. The townspeople laughed and clapped, and ran back to the town and told all the other villagers.

Women started cooking and men started arranging tables outside in the street. Music could be heard for miles around. Late evening you could tell a celebration was going on in the small town. The war was over! They had a reason to celebrate. Although the war had not affected their small town much with the bombing and fighting, they had still lived in fear, and that fact alone had affected their town as food supplies and oil and gas supplies and other things were running extremely low.

Paul and the other men watched from their post and were happy for the Germans as well as for themselves. Some of the townsmen came and invited them to come and eat with them at the celebration. Had the war not been declared over, this could not have happened, but now they were free from restraints of not consorting with the enemy. The man on guard urged them to go ahead, that he would remain on guard. Some of the Americans gathered up what they could to take to the celebration. Oranges and apples, chocolate bars, gum and other treats that the German people had not had very much of. They carried the food down the hill to the town. One of the men took the cloth bag with him for these treats and poured them on the end of one table filled with food as a gesture of peace.

The German children ran over and grabbed the candy and even the women came and grabbed some of the fruits. Fruit had been very scarce there.

"Here, take some," Dailey said to the women who acted afraid of the soldiers, but you could tell by the look in their eyes, that they would love to have some fruit.

"There's plenty here to go around." Paul held out fruit for the ones who would not respond to Dailey's comment. These people did not know these men and new friends were not easy to make, especially when they spoke a different language.

"Here," he said, "Enjoy."

One young female came and picked up some of the fruit and she looked at Paul with solemn, but thankful eyes, and slowly turned and sat back down. Paul smiled at her to show that he was being friendly.

"Fruit is good for you." He knew that she could not understand, but he said it anyway.

The little girl who had been peering at Paul was sitting along the table eating one of the candy bars. Paul waved at the little girl, remembering her as she had sat at the fence post peering at him.

"You remember me? Don't you?" he asked the child. "What's her name?" Paul asked. Some of the townspeople spoke bits of English.

"Sonya," one woman replied. "Kleine Sonya." Paul smiled at her and waved again, and the little girl waved back.

That night they ate with the German villagers. It wasn't grand cuisine, for the Germans only had essential types of food, but it was good regardless, and everyone ate like they had not had for along time. Finally with this war over, the oppression that had surrounded their daily lives would be lifted. Food and supplies would be plentiful again. Long before dark, it was time to go back to the post. But this time the American soldiers felt as if they had friends near. There were a few that spoke English well enough that they communicated fairly well.

As the men lay in their cots that night, there was lots of chatter in the darkness; some of the men talked aloud, as the thoughts of going back to the United States ran through their minds. How good it would be to be back on American soil. Paul only wished it had been sooner—that he wouldn't have had to lose his unit, or kill all those Germans. If the townspeople of Fahrenzhausen knew that he had killed the German soldiers they probably would have not even let him sit at their table. He had not told any of the men here in this new unit what had happened, and he did not intend to. It was his private agony and he would just have to learn to live with it.

Paul was on post the next few days and sat quietly on his bucket till a car or truck would come rumbling along. Things were a little more relaxed now and the demeanor of the people that drove these vehicles seemed a little more friendly.

The unit had not heard anything from their commander about the war other than that it was over. They waited patiently to find out if they were to continue with this assignment or not. Little Sonya came up and sat with Paul on this day. He got a smaller bucket and turned it upside down just like his and put a rag across the top so that she would not get her dress dirty.

"Sprechen sie Deutsch?" she asked Paul.

"Nein kind," he replied.

So they just sat there together quietly. Every so often he would speak to her in English and she would nod like she understood him, but he knew she did not understand. Sonya would eat her treats that Paul would give her, but would still sit with him for hours just sitting there with Paul. He would sit on his bucket and her on hers. For some reason, little Sonya seemed fascinated with Paul, and she would sing little songs while sitting there with him, and Paul would listen even though he did not know the words, and the tune would be something he had never heard. He would pat her on the head, and she would smile at him like she knew it was a sign of affection towards her.

One day Sonya was sitting with him and a young woman marched up the hill as if she was mad. It was the young woman with the solemn eyes. "Sonya!" she said as she got up close to her. Sonya looked afraid and Paul felt sorry for her. This woman was fussing at her in German and reached to grab her arm. Paul reached out and caught the woman's arm to stop her.

"Bitte," the woman started. "Ihre Mutter will sie zu Hause."

Paul let go of her arm and patted Sonya on the head, as if he was telling her to go on. This young woman looked at Paul and smiled. "Danke," she replied.

Paul watched Sonya and this young woman walk back to town. Paul wondered who this young woman was, she was childlike herself, with her pigtails but lovely as well, and he wondered what her relationship to Sonya was.

Commander Bridges came by to talk to the unit a few days later and gave the men their usual pep talk. Today he had a letter for each of them from the commander who was in charge of the southern campaign of the war. He explained to them that even though the war was over, they were taking on a new role of border patrol until they could replace them with an permanent guard patrol. When that would be, he said he was not sure; it could be months or even a year. This dampened the men's spirits somewhat, for they had been hoping their jobs here were about over, and that they would be going back home.

That night Paul wanted to write his mother a letter and told her that yes indeed the war was over, but that he wouldn't be home anytime soon, and he couldn't tell her anything still. The letters were being censored and if he told her anything it would just be blacked out and she wouldn't know anything anyway. So he just started his letter as always, "Somewhere in Germany."

6
Fahrenzhausen

obert came back and joined the unit a few weeks later, bringing a truck with him for the men's use. He was still healing his wound but capable of light duty, so he returned. Paul was glad to see him and asked him not to mention the Battle of Appenrode to the other men. Of course Robert was shocked that Paul didn't want them to know because of the honor he would be bestowed for his actions in warfare, but honored Paul's request. Robert brought Paul a package from their unit commander, Commander Lewis who had been their unit commander before coming to Fahrenzhausen.

Paul took the package into the tent, grateful that he was alone, and the other men out doing other things. He sat on his cot and opened the package. Inside was an accommodation award and a letter from the Commander congratulating Private Paul Crook for winning a bronze star for heroism. Paul looked at the little navy blue box that held the bronze star, and felt of its leather case. He couldn't believe that he had actually received an award for killing people, and he didn't feel right about the fact that it belonged to him for that reason. Paul stuffed the letter and the little box that held the award back into the package and put it in his duffle bag, out of site. He didn't want this award, and so he certainly didn't want anyone else to know about it. He put it away out of site and wanted to forget about it.

Paul joined Robert back outside for it was a beautiful morning. Coffee was still on the cook stove and Robert had a cup and Paul fixed him some eggs on the stove and burned him some toast. Robert filled Paul in on what had happened to him since they had last seen each other.

"So what are we supposed to do here in this scrubby little patch of Germany?" Robert asked Paul, looking around. It was a remote area, not near anything except the little town below and the road that came through there. It was a nice enough place, but with lots of scrubby bushes and the roads were dirt.

"We are to act as border patrol for now," Paul replied. "Anyone heading down this road to München, we are supposed to stop and look at their papers and question them about where they are going. If we feel suspicious of anything, then we are to search their truck or vehicle to make sure they are legitimate, and not trying to smuggle anything into München like guns or any other type of weapons. Anyone coming through the town towards the west, we are not supposed to bother except to check their papers to make sure they are not German military."

They saw an influx of refugees walk through from one country to another, since the war was over, trying to get back to their homes, hoping their homes still stood and going this route north and west. People pulled wagons with their meager belongings piled high and coming thru with their families. They didn't have much, just what they could carry, and it was most of the people's only possessions. The men in the unit watched the refugees walk by and if they needed to, they would stop someone; but they were only to check their papers of origin and then let them pass if they were going in the opposite direction than München.

Robert and Paul got into the truck and rode through the little town so that Robert could see the quaint little village of Fahrenzhausen up close. The town was quite small, only about fifteen houses and a small shop where they sold cigarettes. They stopped in; Paul had been there once before. There was not much choice of brands and they were expensive, but they purchased some anyway to get them through till their supply truck came around again.

Across the street, Anna Reinoehl peered from a second-story window. She saw the familiar soldier and watched him and the other soldier intently. One of them was the one that little Sonya had sat with. She wondered about him; he was so nice to Sonya and Sonya was so fond of him. Wouldn't he be surprised that little Sonya was going to be leaving Fahrenzhausen? She wanted to explain this to him before Sonya left, but she spoke such little English that she did not know how. Still, she ran downstairs and out the door to see if she could relate the message to him. The two men were coming out of the shop and she almost ran right into Paul.

"Excuse me." Paul said, and then realized it was the girl with the solemn eyes.

"Sprechen sie Deutsch?" she asked.

"Nein", Paul replied. "Sorry." She looked lovely this morning; her hair, normally in pigtails like a little girl, was straight and flowed down and across her shoulders.

Robert explained that he could speak a little Deutsch, and she tried to explain to Robert in German about little Sonya. Paul understood the name Sonya and asked her directly if something was wrong with little Sonya.

Anna spoke partly in German with a little English, or something that sounded a little like English. She tried to tell Robert to explain that Sonya's father had been a Deutsche soldat, and that he had not come back from the war. Sonya's mother Natasha had had triplets just after her husband had left and she needed lots of help with the babies and so she had helped with them but now that Natasha's husband had not returned from the war, and they feared he had been killed or was imprisoned somewhere. Natasha was going to have to move where her family, mother and father lived and because she could no longer stay here. They were so poor, she could no longer feed the children so she would be leaving, taking little Sonya and the triplets with her, just ten miles from here near Ingolstalt. Anna stopped talking for a moment so Robert could explain to Paul.

"What ist dein name?" Robert asked her.

"Anna," she replied. "Anastasia Reinoehl."

Robert told Paul that Anna was trying to explain about little Sonya leaving. He explained everything that Anna had said and Paul understood. He had seen so many people walking he knew that Natasha could not walk ten miles with three babies and little Sonya, and her belongings.

Paul told Robert to tell Anna that when she was ready to move, that he would take them there in the truck.

"Paul says…" Robert started telling Anna what Paul had said.

"Dein name ist Paul?" Anna asked Paul. He just nodded.

Anna got really excited about the gesture of help for Natasha. "Sonyalein liked you, you soldat, und Sonya's father ist soldat," she said. She said she would tell Natasha and she would let them know about the move. Then she ran back to the house.

"So that's why little Sonya spent so much time with me." Paul thought.

"I know I shouldn't have volunteered the truck for helping Germans." Paul started. "But I just couldn't imagine a woman walking ten miles with three babies and a little girl too. If I can do anything to help, I want to, but I suppose it's probably wrong."

"Hey," Robert shrugged, "that's up to you. You've been here longer than I have and you know more about what's going on here."

Paul stood post the next morning. It seemed that more and more refugees came through everyday. These people were dirty, hungry and sad but held a glimmer of hope that their homes would still be standing if the bombing from the allied forces hadn't bombed their areas as they had in Berlin and München.

Some refugees just spat at the American soldiers, but others were friendly and kind. Paul guessed it was just a difference in people. Paul knew that his big heart would get him in trouble here if he was not careful; because he was raised poor himself, he always tried to be kind and generous to folks from all walks of life. He wanted to feed these people and would occasionally give them something that was his and he did not eat himself. Many who came through were displaced Germans; he reminded himself that Germans were supposed to be considered the enemy. But having met the townspeople of Fahrenzhausen, Paul knew there was good in the German people as well.

Horror stories came through the grapevine about Dachau, which was not very far from there. Paul heard about the many bodies of the Jews piled high in shallow graves after being gassed in the gas chambers, not to mention how many had been incinerated. But he pushed those thoughts to the back of his mind. Those people were different. The ones who committed the atrocities were of Hitler's regime and not the every day Germans. Not like the people of Fahrenzhausen.

Little Sonya came to sit with Paul the next morning. Robert came out to meet her, saw what a cute little girl she was and understood why Paul was so fond of the child. He and some of the other men had to go to the next post in the truck to pick up supplies. Paul had asked Robert to see if he could get the supply officer to give them extra so he could send some food with little Sonya's family. Robert said he would see what he could do.

Anna came up the road, and waved to Paul and little Sonya. Paul quickly got another bucket and turned it over, motioning for her to join them.

"Hallo Paul." Anna said as she accepted his offer of the seat. Sonya was glad Anna was there. She liked Anna who had been helping her mother with her and the triplets for about a year now. Anna cared about Natasha like a sister. As they sat on their buckets, Anna and Sonya talked amongst themselves, and Anna took Sonya's pigtails down and combed her hair with her fingers, then braided them again. Every now and then the two would look back at Paul and giggle.

"What is funny?" Paul asked, looking at the young girl and the child next to him. But they would just smile. Paul noticed how motherly Anna was to Sonya. She would miss her when Sonya returned to Ingolstadt; he would too. It was odd how comfortable they all seemed together as they sat here on their buckets, odd that Paul would feel an ease with Anna here. He had been nervous and anxious around other females back home, but he felt so comfortable here. Maybe because he knew he was American and they were German and they couldn't even understand him, and he couldn't understand them either.

Robert returned a few hours later to take his turn at post and told Paul that he had left an extra basket of supplies in the back of the truck. Robert asked Anna if Natasha would be ready to go to Ingolstadt tomorrow around noon when Paul completed his turn at post. She nodded, and said goodbye to Paul and Robert, and went to tell Natasha. Sonya sat with Paul for a while longer and then walked slowly and sadly back down the road to town. She realized it was the last time she would get to sit with her American soldier friend. He had become important to her and she was sad to be leaving.

Paul told the men that he would be gone for a few hours and that he would be back by dinner. The men thought nothing of it, but Robert, who knew what Paul was doing and where he was going, told no one. It could be dangerous if someone were to become suspicious of Paul's motives. The unit commander would not approve; but Paul was a man of his word, so he started out in the truck to Natasha's house. It was a small ivy-covered cottage up on a hill on the back road just behind the little town. You could hardly see Fahrenzhausen from there because of the thick growth and brush. The house sat in the woods, looking small but quaint.

When Paul arrived, Anna was there with her younger brother Niklas, whom she introduced to Paul. They would be helping to load the truck. There wasn't that much to load, just some personal belongings and trunks that were filled with clothing. Natasha wanted to leave most of the furniture, in hopes that she would be able to return home eventually when her husband Rudolph came back. She had high hopes that he was alive in some prison; it would be some time before he was released, she was sure. But she had hope and hope had gotten her this far.

Natasha, the babies, blankets and some furniture, a goat and the trunks were loaded in the back of the truck. Paul felt it would be safer if they were out of site. He helped little Sonya climb over the tail gate and made sure she was comfortable before leaving the house. Anna waved at Niklas and told him to go home and then she got into the front of the truck.

"No," Paul started, "you stay here."

"Me go," she insisted in broken English.

"It might be dangerous." He went around and opened the truck door and signaled her to get out. She shook her head no.

"O.K. then," he relented and jumped up into the seat.

The truck rumbled down the road until they reached the first intersection, right in Fahrenzhausen. Anna leaned over so that none of the townspeople would see her as they rode through the intersection and out of town. Then she sat back up and Paul laughed at her. She looked at him, smiled and laughed also. The scenery on the country road was beautiful here as they rode by plowed fields and alongside the Ampere river. It reminded Paul of the farm land in Tails Creek, although the hills here were not like the mountains of Ellijay.

Paul wasn't quite sure how to get to Natasha's house but Anna would tap his arm and indicate when there was a turn to make.

He would look over at Anna as she looked out of the big truck windows; such a pretty young woman, unlike any at home, he thought. The young girls at home were plain, but Anna was different. She looked so innocent in those pigtails but lovely, too, especially as he was remembering the other morning when he had saw her with her hair down.

"Mein Freund?" he asked. He was trying to make conversation. She looked at him wondering what he meant. "Sie" he pointed to her. "Sie mein friend?"

"Ja." she said as a smile came slowly across her face. "Ich Freund."

Paul smiled back. Inside he felt a strange emotion he didn't ever remember feeling; a warm feeling inside that radiated over his entire body. He didn't understand this feeling, but he felt glad that she was here with him.

Across a hill, before they got to Ingolstadt, they met another American roadblock, just like the one back in Fahrenzhausen. Paul immediately grabbed Anna and pushed her down in the seat, hoping the soldiers hadn't seen her. She didn't move, and the guards at the post, seeing a fellow American soldier, raised the stop and waved the truck through.

After they were well past the roadblock, Paul helped Anna up. He shook his head. He could have gotten into real trouble, if they had made him stop the truck and seen Anna, Natasha and the children in the back of the truck. Now he was sorry he had let her come along. He shouldn't have volunteered at all to take them to Ingolstadt, but his big heart and his kindness might get him into trouble again.

Finally they came to another village. This one was a bit bigger than Fahrenzhausen. Anna showed him the little road to turn down to Natasha's family's home. Chickens scurried out of the way as the big truck rolled up into the yard.

People ran outside onto the porch, scared that the truck was sitting here. Anna got out and explained that they had brought Natasha and the children to them. Paul went around the back of the truck and helped little Sonya out first. Anna took the babies one by one to their grandmother while Paul helped Natasha across the gate of the big truck. Natasha's father helped Paul unload Natasha's things.

When it was time to say goodbye, Anna and Natasha hugged as if they were sisters, and Natasha tried to thank Paul. He gave her the basket of food that Robert had gotten from the supply officer. She and her family were so grateful.

Little Sonya took Paul's hand and pulled him down to her. She hugged his neck; he looked at her sad little face and the tears in her eyes.

"You will be fine." He patted her on the head. "You be a good girl. Goodbye."

The family waved until they were out of sight. Once again Anna sat beside him in the truck. He realized that they would have to go back through the road block again and were relieved as the Americans waved the truck through. The soldiers were used to American trucks coming back and forth and hardly did one stop unless it was the Unit Commander or the supply truck.

Paul breathed a little easier once they went through the road block and he didn't even have to tell Anna to get down in the seat. Her head had touched his leg ever so slightly and he knew he had to make sure she was safe so he was glad they did not have to stop. He felt protective of her; for what reason he was not sure. She was a German and he had not felt protective towards a German since he had arrived here.

Paul drove the truck back to Natasha's house so that the townspeople or the soldiers would not see Anna get out of the truck. He didn't want to cause Anna any trouble and he certainly didn't need any himself. He pulled the truck to a stop and got out. He looked over at Anna and she seemed very quiet, although he didn't know why. Anna slid across the big seat to the driver's door and Paul reached up to help her down since the truck was so tall. She just looked at him with a solemn expression as they came eye to eye as he set her down in front of him.

"Paul," she breathed near him as if she was hoarse or out of breath. "Sie mien Freund?"

He looked deeply into her beautiful eyes, "Ja, Freund," Paul replied. He watched her run down the trail towards Fahrenzhausen and started back to the post.

As she entered her house and ran up the stairs, her mind was in a whirl. She thought she could have been kissed tonight…and almost felt it happen, but something held Paul back. She smiled and put her fingers on her lips as she fell into her own bed. What would it have been like, she wondered to have been kissed by an American soldier?

Paul returned to camp earlier than he thought he would. He explained the other men that he had taken some extra supplies to another post. No one questioned it at all. Soon supper was ready. They all ate together in the tent as night began to fall.

Paul had to stand post that night. As he sat there on his bucket, he watched the town lights go out one by one. He wondered what Anna was doing, and then he looked up at the stars. It was a bright night, the moon was full and he could see across the town and fields by moonlight. His family back home crossed his mind. What a difference a year had made in his life. He was beginning to like it here in Fahrenzhausen and didn't miss home so much.

Over the next week, the influx of refugees became more and more steady, as if the road through Fahrenzhausen was a path home. People camped in the woods at night and resumed their journey again in the day light. Paul was not at all sure they were German or Polish, or another nationality. All he knew was that there were a lot of displaced people traveling through this area.

It was sad that the men couldn't help these people on their journeys. They were there only to stop people when they were going into München, but these people were headed west and north. München was seventeen miles south of Fahrenzhausen. These people were tired, and weary. The old people moved slowly; the children whined and cried for their parents to carry them. Some had made make-shift carts. Others carried their belongings on their backs. Some looked so weary it appeared as if they couldn't walk another mile.

Several men stood post now at a time for there were papers to be checked and people to be cleared to continue through the post. They could be German soldiers for all they knew in disguise, but that's what they were here for.

Anna had not been to the post for a few days. Her papa had forbidden it because there had been strange men walking through the town. So Anna helped her mother in the house, doing chores and spring cleaning. She hoped these people would be gone soon.

Anna had sat in her window sill at one time that day, and watched people going thru the road block. The American soldiers were very busy and had not time to talk to her if she were to go up to talk to Paul. Every now and then she would get a glimpse of him walking from one side of the road to the other. He was a nice man and she liked him. Little Sonya was a good judge of character, Anna thought. She thought of how he looked at her in the truck when they had taken Natasha to her family. He had the deepest brown eyes she had ever seen, and she thought he was handsome in his uniform, even if it was his everyday uniform. She didn't know why she wanted to watch him from out the window, but she did, and she wanted to see where he was, and she wanted to go talk to him, but her papa had forbidden her to leave the house because of all these strange men coming through the town. Paul would protect her, she was sure, if only she could leave the house.

Her mother suddenly yelled at her to get out of the window, and come help her, but before long Anna would find herself back at the window sill again, almost before she even realized it.

Robert came over to Paul's cot and shook him awake.

"Get up, there's trouble in Fahrenzhausen." Robert buttoned his clothes hurriedly. "Get your gun, we are going to have to go down there."

They could hear shouting and the screaming of women. People were out in the street in front of the little shop and in front of the Reinoehl house. Paul grabbed his clothes, pulled on his boots, grabbed his gun and was in the truck with Robert before he really knew what was going on. When the American truck stopped in front of the house, there were people outside listening to the yelling that came from inside the Reinoehl home. Paul and Robert jumped out and drew their guns. Niklas Reinoehl ran out and pointed into the house. There were people in the house other than the Reinoehls and they were yelling at the German family saying they were taking what little the Reinoehls had since it was the Germans who had invaded their country years ago and had taken everything from them. Polish, French, or other nationality, the men were not sure but they had to help the Reinoehl family.

Paul ran into the door and saw Anna and Mrs. Reinoehl in their nightgowns, huddled into a corner of the kitchen. Mr. Reinoehl was pushing one of the invading men away from the women. Robert fired a shot outside and they jerked around to see Paul standing with his rifle aimed at them.

"Get out!" he told the men, motioning to the front door. The men raised their arms and Mrs. Reinoehl and Anna cried with relief. They had feared for their life.

Robert held a gun on the men as they left through the door. There was confusion about what had happened, but Mr. Reinoehl said something in German that Robert understood.

"They were going to take their animals." Robert told Paul. "Their horses, pigs and cows and anything else they could find of value."

"They are not taking anything if I can help it," Paul declared.

"Get in the truck," he motioned to the men.

"Robert, you drive and I will guard these three vandals. We will take them on their way and dare them to do anything else to people on their journey."

Robert drove the truck about twelve miles above Fahrenzhausen. He pulled over near a field. Paul motioned for the men to get out and Robert spoke to them in German hoping they could understand that if they came back to Fahrenzhausen they would go to a prison camp. The men stood looking after the truck while Paul and Robert headed back towards the little town.

Mr. Reinoehl stopped the truck and thanked the soldiers. The women had been so scared, he told them. But now they were fine, thanks to Robert and Paul. Paul looked through the door to see if he could see Anna, but she was not to be seen. Paul got out of the truck and walked around to the front of the house to the door.

"Paul, he said they were O.K." Robert called to Paul as he saw that Paul was not convinced that Anna was O.K.

Paul stuck his head inside the door; no one was around. "Anna!" Paul said loudly. "Anna!" he called again. Anna came running down the stairs, now fully dressed. She saw Paul's face and saw he was concerned about her and her mother.

"Me guter, Paul." she said, and relief showed on his handsome face. She walked to where he stood in the door and smiled.

"Are you sure? Those men didn't hurt you did they?"

"Nein, danke." The smile on her face convinced Paul that she was fine, and that he need not worry about her. He waved goodbye, turned and went back out and got into the truck. Mr. Reinoehl invited Paul and Robert to dinner the next night as a thank-you and they gratefully accepted.

As Anna and Mrs. Reinoehl prepared the meal the next day, Anna asked her mother if it would be all right if she was seated across the table from Paul. She explained to her mother that they were friends because of little Sonya and that she now found that she was quite fond of him. Anna's mother was a bit surprised but thought it would be all right. There are worse things my daughter can do than fall for an American soldier, Mrs. Reinoehl thought. As a matter of fact, she might even encourage it, for if Anna were to marry an American soldier she could go to live in America and escape this God-forsaken, war-torn, impoverished country. She asked Anna how much she liked this Paul, and Anna said very much, that he had made her laugh for the first time in a long time. He was nice, she told her mother, and he was kind, and also very good looking.

Josiah Reinoehl came home from the gardens early to help the women prepare for their company. Mrs. Reinoehl caught him at the door and pulled him upstairs so Anna would not hear her speak to him. She told him that their Anna had fallen for this American Soldier, Paul, the one that was coming to dinner. She told Mr. Reinoehl that she had seen the feelings for him in Anna's eyes when she spoke of him.

"How could this be?" he wondered. Mrs. Reinhoehl explained that she wanted to encourage their relationship. They loved their daughter. Even if it meant her going to America, Anna would at least be in a better place.

"You should think about this," he warned. "Our Anna would leave, and may never get to come home to Fahrenzhausen again."

"But who knows," she responded. "Maybe we could go to America and live near her, if she were to marry this Paul. What does she have here? Not a thing. There she could have a brighter future, for it's a great big country."

Mr. Reinoehl nodded. "I will not encourage it, but I will not discourage them either," he told her.

Paul, Robert, Dailey and Bob came for dinner that night. The Reinoehls had a big table already set up for their guests and were very social towards the men. The men looked forward to a home-cooked meal, even though Bob was a good cook in his own right.

He fed the men good meals but they were all ready for something that felt like real home cooking. Mrs. Reinoehl brought out a variety of crusted breads, soup like nothing had ever tasted, fish cakes and an apple pie.

They talked over dinner, Mr. Reinoehl asking questions about the army and where they were from.Paul listened with half an ear to what Mr. Reinoehl was saying, noticing instead that Anna looked very lovely as she sat across from him at the table. Her eyes watch him intently as he spoke to Mr. Reinoehl about the farm his mother had just purchased in Ramhurst, Georgia.

Paul didn't tell Mr. Reinoehl that he had sent his mother just about all of his military pay hoping that Adell and his siblings wouldn't starve to death while he was in another country fighting the war. He didn't tell them how he had ironed all the soldiers uniforms before coming to Germany, just to make extra money to send home to his mother. He just told them that he had seventy acres of land that he planned to farm. He hadn't even seen this place his mother, Charles, and Mary, and William had just moved to. All he knew was that there was land and land was important to people who had nothing else. It meant they could always grow food and have animals that they could slaughter for meat. Adell had saved every penny Paul had sent home until she had enough money to purchase this farm and he planned to farm the property and grow crops so that they would never have to go hungry again.

The similarities between the Reinoehls and his own family were uncanny. These people were poor and so was his family. These people had land; if they hadn't had a garden, they would have not been able to eat. He felt good for one thing. The farm was his way to prosper and have something. But here, the Reinoehls would probably go for years till they could have something again—all because of this war.

Mr. Reinoehl told the men of their family's existence during the war. He had been robbed of so much! When things had been really bad and they didn't have any money, he had taken anything they had left that was valuable and a non-necessity and went to München and sold it in the streets for a fraction of its worth, just to buy food, seed and the other things they needed to be able to sustain themselves here in Fahrenzhausen. They probably should have left here at the beginning of the war, he told them, but his family had lived in Fahrenzhausen as long as he could remember. They had no where else to go.

Robert told of how he had grown up; that life had been really good for him, He had had the chance to go to college but had joined the Army instead, just to spite his father. When he got back, however, he vowed that he was going to go to college and get his degree after all. He wanted to be a doctor, and he promised that he would become a doctor someday.

Paul felt at home here with the Reinoehl family. Little Niklas, Anna's younger brother, didn't say much; maybe he was afraid of the soldiers but he seemed to be a nice boy, much younger than Anna, about seven or eight years old.

After dinner, the soldiers thanked the family for their kind generosity and said their good-byes. It was Robert's turn to stand post, and they had to be getting back. So he left Paul with the Reinoehls. Mr. and Mrs. Reinoehl were cleaning up and Niklas was sent off to bed. Paul asked Anna if she would like to go for a walk. Anna told her mother that they were going down the street a bit, but would not be gone very long.

They walked in front of the other row of houses and in front of the little shop, and then made the turn up to the hill. It was starting to get a little dark outside, but they had enough light to see where they were going.

Paul took Anna's hand and held it as they walked. She smiled and the years of war felt as if they melted away as he held her small hand in his much larger one. He made her feel special and evidently she made him feel the same. Paul had never been in love, and he wasn't sure what it felt like, but he knew this was a special feeling. This was a magical evening, something new to him, and a warm sensation ran over him; he felt like something was becoming of this friendship with Anna, even though he understood little of what she said.

She spoke with her eyes and the way she smiled at him. That morning he had been so concerned for her welfare. He had saved her family from the refugees that had threatened their existence. He knew from that smile that she was fond of him, and suddenly he realized he was fond of her as well.

Anna would try to explain something to Paul; he could understand some of it by her gestures but he could not understand everything. He would laugh at the way she would motion as she talked and she would laugh with him. He saw a wild flower on the side of the road and he picked it and handed it to her. She smelled it and looked at him with eyes of wonderment. The flower was purple, but resembled a daisy. Paul thought of a little game they played as children.

Paul stood before her, and picked off one petal at a time. "She loves me, she loves me not. She loves me, she loves me not. She loves me, she loves me not. She loves me."

Somewhere in Germany

It was the last petal and it's significance expressed everything he was feeling.

"She loves me!"

7
The Beginning of Fall in Fahrenzhausen

Niklas Reinoehl came to the post and sat with Paul on Sonya's bucket. Niklas was a good boy, but not like Sonya. Paul missed little Sonya. She had been special to Paul because she had taken his mind away from the tragedy that had played out on the road to Appenrode. She had put a ray of sunshine back into his heart just about the moment when he thought life was cold and the lives of the men in his old unit had been snuffed out for nothing. Sonya had came along—a little bouncy ray of sunshine that made him believe that life was not about all bad, but the nice and unexpected surprises as well.

Paul told Niklas stories of back home, about when he was a little boy himself. He had all but forgotten about his childhood, being here in this land, but remembered a story of how once, when he was in the cemetery by the church, he had climbed up on a large tombstone and it fell on him and crushed his chest. For a long time after that, his ribs hurt and he had trouble breathing. Why he told Niklas that story, he did not know, and what Niklas understood about that story, Paul did not know that either. He really did not feel as if Niklas was even listening. Little Sonya had listened, but he didn't seem as if he was for he was too interested in other things.

Niklas was a mischievous child and would play with the grass hoppers that hopped around in the grass. Paul just assumed Niklas was a typical boy, distracted by any creature of God that he came upon, any adventure he could hope to find.

Paul asked Niklas where Anna was. The boy tried to explain to him that she had gone to Natasha's house, to clean up some of the mess that the refugees had made when they camped out in Natasha's house one night. The refugees passed through less and less frequently now and Paul wondered when the last of them came, if the unit would still be needed to stand post here.

When Paul left post and Dailey took over, he walked the trail behind the town that went through the woods to Natasha's house. Anna was there and looked quite the mess with the rag in her hair and smudges on her apron and clothing.

"Hallo," she smiled and waved when she saw Paul's handsome face.

"Hello," he smiled. "I'm here to help you."

Paul straightened what he saw was in disarray, and Anna scrubbed the floors with a brush to get rid of the mud the refugees had tracked in. Natasha might be able to return home when there would be news of Rudolph, and Anna wouldn't want poor Natasha to see her home in this shape.

Anna got a sense of being here with Paul as if it was their house and they were cleaning together. A smile slowly crept over her face as she sat on the floor, her dress flowing around her legs.

Paul noticed that smile, and at that moment, he felt something stir inside of himself he had never felt before. Anna was beautiful and he could never forgive himself if he never got to kiss her. So, he did. He went over and pulled her up to him, and kissed her, tilting her chin up to meet his. He was much taller than her and she had to stand on her tiptoes to reach him. He put his arms around her and rubbed her back, she felt so right in his arms. Anna pulled back and looked at him and him at her. She knew there, this moment she was falling in love with Paul Crook.

Paul became like a member of the Reinoehl family. He was there always, helping Mr. Reinoehl work in the gardens. Paul shared his gardening secrets with Mr. Reinoehl, bringing vegetables and fruits that they didn't have, so that they would have something different to try. Late in the evenings he and Anna would spend lazy hours that seem to last forever, either at the house, or walking through the fields and the valleys of this beautiful land. Sometimes they walked to Natasha's house where they could be intimate and alone and share their love.

Anna gave Paul two pictures of herself made in München in 1944, when she was just sixteen. It was the only ones she had. She wished she had another more recent picture, when she was much more grown up, but war had prevented them from doing normal things and she had not been to München in a very long time. She wanted him to have a picture of her, and he was happy to have them. She looked much younger in the pictures, but he put them in his wallet and told her that he would keep them always.

Late at night, at post during the dark hours, Paul would sit and stare at the moon and stars and wonder where this love would take him and Anna. It was a wonderful time of night when he could hear the crickets chirping and the feel the cool breeze, his his favorite time to sit and think about life. He was shocked at himself for his behavior with Anna, but when he thought of her, he couldn't resist. She was a weakness to him and he had fallen in love with her. He knew she was in love with him also, because she had given herself to him fully with no expectations or reserve.

It was August now, and summer was fading quickly. Neither one realized how much time they had spent together because everything felt so new to them as it always does when people first fall in love. He would not allow thoughts of home to enter his mind, because home meant leaving here and Anna. He didn't want to think about that right now. He had not even written his mother for weeks because he knew if he did, he would be drawn back into the world of his past, and he didn't want to leave the thoughts of the love that he and Anna shared.

Anna would come to post and sit with Paul, sometimes when they did not expect the Unit Commander to come around. Robert and Dailey would sometimes talk to her, which made Paul a little jealous, for they could speak a little German and he could hardly speak any. They would have a conversation with Anna and he had no idea what they were saying. He would almost become tense, wondering whether she preferred talking to them, men who could understand her while he could not understand a lot of what she was talking about.

Paul spent as much time as he could with Anna when possible, even though Paul and the men in the unit seemed to always have something to do. Occasionally he and Robert, or Dailey would have to go into München to get supplies. The supply truck would run most of the time, but when supplies were low they made a special trip to pick up food, and what ever they needed till the next truck ran.

They got a real good look at the war torn areas by these short trips, and they could see the destruction that war caused. The bombed areas were almost completely devastated to the point of nothing existed, but sometimes, there were areas just after the bombed areas, that looked almost completely normal.

In September, the Unit Commander came around the post for inspection. He still gave them no word about when their mission here would end. The refugees had been long gone and now the streets seemed so much safer. But their mission would continue. They were given word that a more permanent post would be set up and that new supplies would come in. They were to build a new building and erect a more stable border stop. At some point in time, a border patrol would be permanently installed here at this very location and the occupation of American troops in Germany would be there for a long time, the Commander had told them. A small barracks would be built to house the men because the tents would not be suitable for winter.

When the supplies arrived in late September. the barracks had to be built quickly as winter weather was approaching. This took a lot of time and there wasn't much opportunity for Paul to be with Anna. Just a few hours here and there every week until the barracks would be completed.

More and more Paul wanted Anna to understand completely what he was saying to her; deep down he knew that if she ever was to come to America, that she would need to be able to speak English. He had heard that English lessons were being taught over in a little community between Fahrenzhausen and Ingolstalt. He suggested Anna take lessons and Mr. And Mrs. Reinoehl were in favor of it. Mrs. Reinoehl considered this gesture a token of the love Paul had for their daughter and thought that he would most probably ask Anna to marry him.

Paul traded post duty with someone else if it interfered with taking Anna for the lessons. It was becoming quite cold now and they would bundle up and carry a blanket for warmth, since the truck had no heat. The lessons were taught once or twice a week in a small school house in the community of Massenhausen. It took a while to drive but the trip was worth it, because Anna was eager to learn and could make out a few words of language in English after a week or two. They enjoyed the drive there, they encountered no road blocks and Anna could sit next to him in the truck; Paul's closeness and the fact that they were just together seemed to reassure Anna of his feelings for her. She would kiss his hands, and later on the way back to Fahrenzhausen, they would pull to the side of the road and be with each other in a way that the two of them wanted to be.

In November, the men in the unit went to the Reinoehls for dinner after Paul had explained to them the American tradition of Thanksgiving. Mr. Reinoehl killed several of his largest hens for the occasion and Mrs. Reinoehl made many of the soldier's favorites. Of course, there were always wonderful crusty breads with homemade butter and honey. Even though it was a American tradition, the German family enjoyed celebrating with the men tremendously.

Robert could see the love between Paul and Anna. When the two were together, it was quite evident. He wondered how either of them thought this love could survive, but said nothing because he owed Paul his life. Still, he was concerned for the both of them.

Anna was learning small sentences to put together in English when they had been going to lessons for about two months. She was smart, a good student and eager to learn as quickly as possible. One particular time, Anna told Paul to wait outside for her in the truck. She wanted to talk to her teacher.

When they were on their way back home, she knew they were near Fahrenzhausen, and she motioned him to stop. She snuggled close to him and said, "Ich liebe dich." She had spoken the words before, but this time she was trying to say something more. "I love you," she said in English. It was the first time Paul had heard the words from a woman other than his mother or sister, and Anna had said it in English! He did not say it back to her, because he did not feel it was appropriate just because she had said it to him. Instead he kissed her on the lips and said "Danke."

8
A Dangerous Mission

*L*ate one evening, an American truck came by the post. The people inside called upon the soldiers to come and help with a situation they were having in a town near Fahrenzhausen. Robert, Dailey and Paul volunteered for this mission. They loaded their guns, took some extra ammo, and grabbed the gear they thought they needed and took off. There was no time to let anyone know what was going on, and if Anna was to inquire about where Paul was, then the other men in the unit could inform her that Paul had went on a mission. So Paul did not worry about telling Anna.

The people in the truck that had come by the post had told Dailey that there were some vigilante immigrants that had raided the neighboring town of Karlsfeld. They had taken the women hostage and had presented demands of the men in the city. If these demands were not met they would not release the women.

It had become an explosive situation and several other units sent soldiers as well. The men drove though valleys and farms, and small towns until they neared Karlsfeld. As they approached, they could see several American trucks sitting at the edge of town. Robert, Dailey and Paul looked for the commander, but there was none. Several men sat in a barn, waiting on troops to arrive. They were trying to work out a plan for the rescue of the women, and to undermine these vigilantes.

"What can we do to help?" Robert asked. "We heard there was trouble here and came from the post at Fahrenzhausen. So can you fill us in on what's happening?"

"There are men in the church building who have taken about twenty-four women hostage. The townsmen are threatening to storm the church and take control but the vigilantes swear they will kill the women. We have an out-of-control situation, and I have told the townsmen that we are working on a plan. They are meeting us here in a few hours and we are going to try to devise a plan to keep the women out of harm's way."

The men considered various approaches they might take as they waited for the German men to arrive. One of the men there had the best idea, and they thought it would be the best approach and solution to tell the German men, and see if they agreed. These were these German men's wives and daughters, so naturally they were angry and worried that the men would actually kill some of the women. They feared making the vigilantes angry enough to do that. The situation called for a very tactful approach.

When the German men came, the Americans explained the plan. They would wait till morning. When they took the supplies of food the men were demanding they would ambush them, try to isolate them from the women, and overpower the men. The German men agreed that it could work, if that at the same time they and the Americans would attack the back of the church and release the women before they could be in danger of any gunfire. So they had a plan, and it could work if the men in the church were all at the front when they opened the door for the supplies. Hopefully no one would get hurt. The last thing any of the men wanted was for any women and girls to be killed.

That night they slept in the barn, among the cows in from the pasture. The men did not have blankets or a change of clothing but they were comfortable as they lay in the hay as a makeshift bed. A few chickens ran around and the clucking noise they made was annoying but after awhile they roosted on the rafters of the barn, and everything became quiet.

The morning sun came through the cracks of the barn wood, and woke the men even before the rooster crowed. They gathered all of their belongings into the truck and prepared for the rescue. Before approaching the church they went over the plan once more, with the German men saying that all cost they needed to protect the women. The American soldiers agreed that it was the most important thing, and they promised to try with all their might to get the women out safely.

Several of the German townsmen took the supplies to the front door of the church for the men who were holding the hostages. When the doors were opened, Robert and some of the other American men from other units were to overcome the men inside the church while the back door was being broken down. The other Americans, including Paul and Dailey would get the women out. Robert and the men stood firm at the corners of the church just out of sight from anyone opening the door, and when the German townsmen knocked with the supplies in hand, the door opened as planned. Swiftly, the signal was given to storm the back door while Robert and the other Americans attacked the men holding the hostages. As soon as they had the men at the door under control, the rest went in the back door and told the women to hurry and get out. There was one vigilante in the back of the church but he was unarmed and immediately surrendered to the soldiers as soon as he saw they were armed. The plan had worked wonderfully and soon the women were freed. Some had been put into a room by themselves and locked in. These women said the reason they were put in there was because they had caused the vigilantes trouble. The German women laughed and said that they were tough old birds and the men didn't know what to do with them because they were trying to fight their way out of the situation.

When Paul saw who some of these men were, he was not surprised. They were some of the same men that had tried to steal the animals from the Reinoehls in Fahrenzhausen. They had warned them then that they would go to a prison camp, and Paul kept his word as he loaded them up in the truck and headed them for a camp that he knew of just west of there. It might take extra time to deliver them, but these men were repeat offenders and they deserved to be in a prison before something awful happened. Robert told Dailey to ride back with the other men; they could drop him back at the post of Fahrenzhausen on their way. Paul and Robert would transport the vigilantes to the prison where they belonged. He told Dailey to let the other men know that they would be back in a day or so. As the prisoners were loaded up into the truck, Paul noticed one of them was soaked with sweat, and pale looking. He didn't know if this man was just over dressed, but he looked sick to him.

The German townsmen and the women whom they had rescued came and thanked them for their help. They gave them a basket of food for their trip to the prison. These people didn't want to see these vigilantes again either, and were glad to be rid of them.

The Americans had never been to this area of Germany before, and a lot of the countryside was beautiful. They drove for miles and miles; they came to a more wooded area, and neared a larger town, finally arriving at the prison. It was late evening and they had driven almost all day. As the prisoners were unloaded, Paul again noticed the one that seemed to be sick. He was perspiring and looked pale and grim. Paul told the guard that he thought that one of the prisoners might be sick and he may want to isolate him until they determined what was wrong with him. Robert and Paul was glad this mission was over; what could have turned out to be a bad situation had worked out well and everyone got out of it safely. These vigilantes wouldn't be bothering anyone else for a good long while.

Robert and Paul spent the night on the prison grounds, sleeping in the back of the truck. They were on their way back to Fahren-zhausen before most people awoke; they believed they would reach the little town by mid-afternoon. But as they drove along the dirt roads, Paul noticed he wasn't feeling very well. He began to sweat and felt feverish and nauseous. He pulled over to the side of the road and vomited, and asked Robert if he would drive. He wondered if he could have gotten food poisoning from the food that the Germans sent with them the day before, but, remembering the prisoner who was perspiring so much, Paul decided that what ever he had, he very well might have gotten from him.

Somewhere in Germany

The further they drove, the sicker he felt. Before they got back to Fahrenzhausen, Paul had become so sick that he was almost delirious with fever.

When the truck pulled into the camp, Robert got out and got some of the other men to come out and to carry Paul into the tent. They put him on his cot, and covered him up for he was chilled and visibly shaking. Hot and cold at the same time, Paul was perspiring intensely. Robert got a bowl of cool water and a cloth and soaked the cloth in the cool water and wrung it out and placed it on Paul's head. He then went outside, and talked to the other men about Paul.

"I have no idea what's wrong with Paul, but he is extremely sick. I don't know what to do," he told them. "It started on our trip back. I don't know if it's the flu or a more severe medical problem."

"Should we go to another post and see if there's a medic? Who's going to take care of him? The way he looks, I don't want to be around him and get it myself," one of the other men said.

"No. I don't think that's necessary. I can take care of him. I owe that man my life. But it might be a good idea if no one else goes around him, he is probably contagious. We will pull the cots out of the tent for tonight and see if he is better tomorrow."

Robert went back to change the rag occasionally. He saw that Paul was somewhat delirious. It was like he was incoherent but muttered in his sleep, so Robert was sure it was all a result of the fever. He decided to go get Anna or Mrs. Reinoehl and see if they would know what to do for him.

Robert told Anna and Mrs. Reinoehl about Paul's sickness. Anna immediately ran up the hill and into the tent and went to Paul's side. Mr. and Mrs. Reinoehl came up the hill with Robert and went into the tent where Paul lay and Anna sat beside him. When they saw how sick he was they warned Anna that it might not be a good idea that she was sitting so close.

She told them that she would not leave his side until he was better. Mrs. Reinoehl saw that he was running a very high fever, and she took Mr. Reinoehl and went back to their house. Mr. Reinoehl came back about an hour later with an elixir of herbs that Mrs. Reinoehl had made up that might possibly help Paul. He gave it to Anna with instructions, and a salve that she was to rub on his chest. They said that if she wanted to stay with him, it would be O.K. since the other men were not sleeping in the tent that night.

Anna stayed by Paul's side except for a break or two outside for a breath of fresh air. She did not fear his condition, and took great care of him, changing the cool rags often to reduce his temperature. She was worried because he had been so incoherent for so long now, and not himself.

Paul talked in his sleep every so often, as the fever raged in his body.

She put the salve on his chest, and it reeked of medicine or herbs, but she knew that her mother was good with these things and would know how to help Paul get better. If his fever would break, she was certain that he would be fine. Anna sat up late into the night taking care of Paul, and never slept herself. The night was long, and she could hear the snoring of the men as they slept on cots outside the tent.

Every minute seemed to last hours; she was so worried that she would not go home and leave him for even one minute. She sat on a trunk by his bed all night long and when she felt herself starting to doze, she would immediately snap out of it, and tend to him again.

Paul was sick for the most of the next day. Mrs. Reinoehl came in the morning and saw how wet he was from the perspiration. She said that he was sweating the poison out of his system and the herbs were responsible for that. She brought soup and something she had mixed up for Anna to see if she could get him to drink. If they could get this elixir in him and he could hold it down, it would definitely help. Mrs. Reinoehl had not had all the ingredients the night before, but borrowed them from another woman in the town this morning.

They raised Paul up on the cot, and gave him sips of this elixir. He moaned and coughed and almost got sick, but they patiently spent the time it would take to get the elixir down and finally laid him back down on the cot.

Mrs.Reinoehl told Anna it should work, and when he was feeling better to get him to give him some of the soup she had brought.

Robert came in and checked on Paul. He told Anna to go home and get some rest and that he would take care of him, but she refused to leave.

Robert didn't argue with her, but knew that she was tired because there were shadows under her solemn eyes.

Paul's fever broke later that day, and Anna was sitting by his side when he opened his eyes. He reached up and felt the rag on his head, and he pulled it off.

"I've been sick," he told Anna. She smiled and went to go get Robert and let him know that he was awake. Robert came in and saw Paul and told him that Anna had stayed by his side all night, and that Mrs. Reinoehl had gotten him well with her elixir.

Anna was so happy that he was awake and felt better. She fed him the soup, and before late evening he was sitting up and talking to her. He had had the flu, and now he just hoped that Anna, Robert or Anna's family wouldn't come down with it.

9
Christmas
in Germany

ecember came all too quickly and the men in Paul's unit were glad for the barracks they had started building two months ago, and had moved into only weeks ago. The tent would have never kept out the cold they now experienced. They had even had a dusting of snow one night which, though light, bore a promise of more to come.

December meant nothing much to Paul; a few days before Christmas, they went to town and shopped. They put up a little tree the day before Christmas Eve, with a few ornaments, and popcorn and cranberries strung on a string around it for decoration. The year of his father's death in 1935 had been a very hard year for his mother Adell, and on Christmas day there were no real presents, just an orange and a couple pieces of candy stuck in the stockings that hung over the mantel. Mary had only been five years old and she was convinced that Santa Claus must have thought she was a bad girl, which was why he had brought her so little. Paul thought about how sad she had been that year and swore that he would make it up to her someday, but he was not home this year for Christmas and the likelihood of being there next year was uncertain. The Reinoehls were in the same shape as his family had been in 1935. How would they provide for Christmas this year?

It was December the 5th, and Paul went to the Reinoehl house late in the evening. There on the door step was a boot that he thought someone had forgotten. It looked about the size of Niklas, so he picked it up and carried it inside with him. There, Niklas saw that he had the boot in his hand, and he took it from him with a frown on his face and took it back outside and sat it on the stoop again.

Anna laughed at little Niklas for she knew he was waiting for Nikolaustag. She explained to Paul that in their country they had a tradition that on the 5th of December. You put a boot out on your front porch, and on the morning of December the 6th— if you had been good—Nikolaus would bring you holiday treats. If you had been bad, he would only leave you twigs. Paul wondered if Niklas would get treats. Did the Reinoehls have something to put in Niklas' boot?

After Niklas went off to bed, Paul asked Anna if they could walk over to the little shop. There he told Anna to get some treats for Niklas and she picked out a few. Paul picked up a whole bunch more candies and then he paid for them. Anna knew what he was doing and she thought he was very kind and caring. When they went back to the Reinoehl house, they saw that Mrs. Reinoehl had stuck a few cookies wrapped in a cloth inside Niklas' boot. Anna and Paul put their treats inside and the boot was brimming over the top. Niklas would think he had been a very good boy.

Two weeks later, the weather turned brutal, and the men got a taste of snow like they had never saw before. The heavy snow fell all night, and much into the day the next day. It was hard for them to even get outside the barracks, the snow was so deep, much less stand post in the shack. But later in the day, when the snow stopped, they went back to standing post even though there was hardly any traffic. The Germans may have known how to maneuver in this kind of weather, but the men in the unit were not used to this deep of a snow, so they did not get out in the truck on this day.

The supply truck ran one day after Paul had stood his post, and Paul asked the driver if he was going into München. The driver said that he would be going near München but not all the way into town. Paul asked if he could ride along. It was his chance to get Anna something for Christmas and he couldn't pass up this opportunity and wind up empty-handed later. She had been so good to him he wanted to get her something special.

The driver dropped Paul off in a place where there were some shops; among the ruins of München, some areas were still in tact and up and running their businesses. Paul told the driver to pick him up on his trip back toward that way. Paul wandered around a few shops and noticed the store keeper's eyes following him. They should be used to American soldiers by now for there were many in München.

First he bought Mr. Reinoehl some cigars. Although Mr. Reinoehl didn't really smoke, he had enjoyed a cigarette with Paul from time to time. Paul thought he would enjoy the cigars for they were flavored with different flavors. For little Niklas, he found a "Johnny Jump-up"—a little man carved out of wood, very realistic looking, on a stick. Out of the bottom of the stick you would pull a string and the man would dance. This would be a delight to Niklas, because Paul noticed that he didn't have any toys. For Mrs. Reinoehl he bought a Christmas decoration, a Christmas Pyramid, one like he had never seen. It must have been a German tradition. It was a wood carved three-tiered piece with paddles on the top; you placed candles on the bottom and when lit, the heat from the candles made it turn and the little men on the top would go round and round. His mother would likely enjoy this herself, so he was sure Mrs. Reinoehl would like it as well.

Paul went from shop to shop to look for something for Anna. He wanted to find something special but he just couldn't find what he was looking for. Everything seemed to be made of wood and it wasn't what he wanted.

Finally on the end of the row of stores something in the window caught his eye. He went in and asked if he could see the piece. It was a little silver heart on a piece of delicate ribbon, much like a necklace. The heart had etchings on it in curls and loops and was quite unique. Anna would like it, he was sure. He looked around the stores for a while longer, bought some holiday cookies and candies to make the Reinoehl's holiday a little more special.

When the supply truck returned, Paul had been waiting for over an hour with his treasures tucked safely in his army jacket. He asked the driver how hard it would be to get a turkey for their Christmas dinner; the driver said he could get anything for a price, but that most Germans families that were still well off had a suckling pig or goose for their dinner for Christmas.

Paul arranged a delivery for the day before Christmas Eve and gave the driver more money than he was supposed to. He told the driver that he hoped that he would have a special Christmas too.

There were a few good days of better weather and Paul's unit had to finish their work on the new border guard-post. They had several days of seriously hard work building ahead of them and Paul didn't really have time to spend with Anna. The Unit Commander had come and supervised some of the work to make sure the government regulations were met. The Army was replacing all these make-shift border patrol posts with more permanent posts.

Certain specifications had to be met and the men wanted to make the Unit Commander happy with their work. These posts would have to last for the duration of the occupation and no one knew just how long that would have to be, maybe years. The war had been over for seven months, but there were still American soldiers all over Germany. Since the stream of refugees had mostly stopped, it was a slower pace here, a few trucks carrying contraband had been taken possession of and the soldiers understood that their mission was still important. Their show of their presence there was worth more to prove to any defiant groups that they should not cause any trouble. The American Army stood their ground and showed their force was not to be reckoned with.

The Unit Commander departed on December 20th. After he had left, Mr. Reinoehl invited all the men to the parade they had for Christmas. It was the night of the 21st and the parade went through the whole town. Not a grand event by big-city standards, but it was attended by all. It ended at the Catholic Church where refreshments would be served. The townspeople wanted to include the soldiers because they had helped them in times of trouble, and they wanted to make them feel like it was a holiday since they were so far from their own home.

The parade didn't really last that long, but the children of the town wore white robes and carried a long pole with a star at the top. Niklas was one of these children, wearing the robes, and Mr. and Mrs. Reinoehl was so very proud of their young son. They sang Christmas carols in German and there was a group of the townspeople that played instruments and followed behind the procession of children as they walked through the little town, all the way to the church. It was cold out; the candles that people carried and the lights on late in the town, just for this occasion made it feel like a special night, like a holiday.

Anna was excited to see Paul for she had not seen him in days and she had news to tell him. She learned from Natasha's family that they had heard news of Rudolph, her husband. He was in a prison camp in northern Germany, but at least he was alive and the father of her children had not been killed as they had feared. Rudolph's father had left home for weeks, and had traveled around northern Germany trying to find out the where about of his son. They had assumed he had been imprisoned but were not sure, and his parents wanted to know if their son was dead or alive. It could be a long time before he came home to Fahrenzhausen, but Natasha was happy that her husband was alive.

On December 23rd, the supply truck came and delivered the suckling pig just as Paul had arranged for the Reinoehl family. Paul happily carried it to the Reinoehl house. Mrs. Reinoehls eyes grew wide with excitement when she saw the pig. It was frozen, but it would have to be cooked right after thawing, so she cleaned a place in the kitchen where it would thaw slowly. Mr. Reinoehl came home for lunch. He had been cutting wood for the long winter, and he was surprised when Mrs. Reinoehl showed him the suckling pig Paul had bought for Christmas Eve dinner. Paul's generosity was so overwhelming to the family, they knew it had to be because of the love he had for their daughter, Anna. It made them proud to know him and they would always think of his kindness rewardingly.

Christmas Eve dinner was for just the family and Paul, for he was like family. Mrs. Reinoehl had decorated the Christmas tree though small with real candles and lit them just before dinner. The dinning room table was exquisite with the cooked suckling pig as a center piece. Mrs. Reinoehl had cooked her traditional braised red cabbage and potato dumplings and there always was a variety of crusted breads, and for dessert she made stollen which was like a fruit cake but a different kind of bread. Although it had crossed Paul's mind about his family back home, it was way too expensive to send anything of any size back to the United States, so he decided that he would have to make it up to them next year.

Tonight was for Anna and her family and he saw that they really enjoyed their meal. It was a rare treat for them to be able to have this kind of food, and it was all because of Paul who was trying to create some joy for them for they had had to live so miserably poor for so long now. They would appreciate him for it, he was sure.

When their dinner was finished and they adjourned to the living area, Mrs. Reinoehl asked Mr. Reinoehl to please play his violin for entertainment tonight. Mr. Reinoehl agreed only because it was a holiday, for he had sworn that he would not play his violin, his one treasure that he had kept when everything else frivolous was sold, until the war was over, and life was good again. He felt guilty for keeping his prized possession, but kept it only because his grandfather had owned it, and played it and taught him to play it when he was just a boy. Mr. Reinoehl played the violin, and as a melody came from the instrument, it seemed a sad but beautiful tune that he delivered from the piece. A tear came from Mrs. Reinoehls eye, for she had not heard the lovely melody for so very long. They all clapped when he was finished, and Mr. Reinoehl got up and bowed in front of the group, and then put away the violin again.

Paul pulled out his gifts. He gave Niklas his first and his eyes lit up when he saw the "Johnny Jump-up." Niklas ran off to his bedroom immediately to play with the toy, after thanking Paul. Mr. Reinoehl was happy with his cigars and lit one immediately, making Mrs. Reinoehl fuss about the smoke choking her as she coughed. But it was Christmas, so she didn't make a real fuss. Mrs. Reinoehl was so proud of her gift that she told Paul she would use it every Christmas for the rest of her life, it brought so much joy to her heart.

Paul asked Anna to go sit in the truck with him outside in front of the house. She agreed, and when he gave her the heart necklace, and put it around her neck, she cried and said that she didn't have anything for him. But Paul did not care. He told her that he loved her for the first time, although she said she knew it, that she had felt it for some time. Paul was a quite man, slow to show his emotions but Anna had never been in love before now and she did not expect much from him. All she knew was that she loved him with all her heart and soul and that was enough for her.

Paul had truly made Christmas Eve special for them and he was happy that he knew these people for they truly were good people. When Paul said good-night to the family, Mrs. Reinoehl sent food for the rest of the men in the unit for the table had been brimming with food, and she wanted the other men to have something as well.

It snowed a heavy snow early January and no one had to stand post on those days because the snow was so heavy that no one could get through the road anyway. The townspeople got out and played in the snow and the men in the unit made a makeshift sled and sledded down the hill into Fahrenzhausen. Paul found time to spend with Anna and Niklas, and they joined the men outside sledding down the hill, and it was one of the best times that they spent together.

10
The Unexpected Departure

The Unit Commander came around early on January 21st, and though the weather had been miserably cold, there had been no more snow. He had come to tell Robert and Paul that they were to report to London in two days for a new mission. This shocked both Paul and Robert because they had felt at home here for so long that neither of them had thoughts of leaving any time soon. But this could be a temporary mission and they both were sure that they would be coming back to Fahrenzhausen soon.

Paul had to tell Anna and the Reinoehls that he would soon be leaving. As soon as the Unit Commander left, he went down to the little town and found them all at home. They understood what he was saying, but suddenly Anna was scared. She was frightened that Paul would not be able to come back.

The good-byes two days later were excruciatingly hard for the two young people in love. Paul had walked down early that morning to spend time with Anna's family, and Anna was quiet and sullen. When Paul asked her what was wrong, she broke down and cried because she was so scared that she would never see Paul again. Paul gave her his address just in case and told her what ever happened he would come back. She cried and cried about his departure but he wanted her not to worry, so he promised her that he would come back to her. He gave her his word, and he always kept his word.

The truck waited on him as he said a final good-bye to Anna. They could not part, clinging together as one as he held her and tried to whisper in her ear that everything would be O.K. She finally let go of him and watched him get into the back of the truck where Robert sat. He too was feeling bad because he knew Anna and Paul were so in love.

The truck started to pull away and Anna ran after it waving, and screaming to Paul but he could not tell what she was saying for they were already out of range. Finally he saw that she dropped to her knees and was sobbing. As the truck turned the corner, and out of site of Fahrenzhausen, Paul felt a lump in his stomach, one that caused great pain, more than he could bear. He turned away from Robert and faced the side of the truck where Robert would not see just how much pain he felt, for a tear was running down his face, and he could not appear this shaken in front of the men on the truck.

Because Paul and Robert had been in a different unit before the battle of Appenrode, they were chosen for this mission. They arrived in London three days later and were told to report to the Port Authority. Their mission would be to prepare equipment, tanks, trucks and other things ready to be shipped out back to the United States. Time went by here quickly for they worked from ten to twelve hours each day getting guns, artillery and belongings of the men loaded into the ships to go on the voyage across the ocean.

Sometimes when a ship would leave port, carrying a load of military men on their journey home, Paul would watch the men on the decks as they left on their trip. He would silently say a prayer for their safe arrival in America.

There was a massive departure of equipment, trucks and men and by and by Paul would think to himself about the enormous amount of things that must have been in Germany. They had sent back so much and the time it took to get each ship ready for departure from the docks was massive. The men boarding the ships going to America were always so happy and gay about going home. But all Paul could think about was returning to Fahrenzhausen and Anna. He hoped his mission here would end soon and they could return to his previous duty.

The two men had little time to see London, but in what time they had, Robert and Paul went to see the sights before they would have to go back. This part of the world was definitely different than his world. Tails Creek was a mere spot on the road compared to some of the sites he had seen here in this foreign land.

Time lingered and it felt as if all of America had been loaded and shipped, because months and months had passed and Paul was ready to go back and join the other men in the unit. He had lost weight, and had not eaten really well for his mind was on Anna and how bad he missed her and wanted to see her and let her know that he was back. From time to time, his mind would go back to the day he left and he would think about how she cried and worried that he would not return. He told her he would come back, and now it was May and he had not returned.

Somewhere in Germany

Paul wished he could talk to Anna to let her know that his time here had continued on a lot longer than he expected. He wanted to tell her that he would be so happy when he got back to Fahrenzhausen and he would be happy to see her again. There was no way to send word, so he had to be content until he was through with their mission in London.

Their former Unit Commander, Commander Bridges sent a telegram to Robert and Paul on May 4th and told them that they would be getting on a ship themselves on May 26th and returning to the States. They were to report to Fort Bragg in North Carolina. Paul told Robert that he wanted to go back to Fahrenzhausen. Robert was sympathetic, because he knew that Paul missed Anna tremendously, but he reminded him that as far as the Army was concerned that Paul was still a soldier of the American Army and they would consider him AWOL if he did not return to the States and report to Fort Bragg as he was supposed to.

Robert was right, but how could he tell Anna? How was he supposed to go back to Fahrenzhausen as he promised if he had to get on a ship and go back to America? He was sick to his stomach. It was the first time he felt that he ever had to go back on his word and it ate him up inside.

On May 26th, Robert and Paul took their belongings to the big ship that was docked for their departure. There they found their names on the list and Paul still could not believe it. He didn't want to believe that he was to get on this ship. Not today or any day. The ships cargo had been loaded a few days ago and they were ready to set sail just a few hours later. Paul stood on the deck, angry at himself for he was torn between leaving this country and going back to the States. Anna was here within reach of London and when he got back to America, she would be a world away. This realization suddenly sunk in with him and he threw up across the rail. All he cared about, the most important thing that had been in his life was waiting for him in Fahrenzhausen, and what would Anna think of him when he didn't come back as he had promised.

They were assigned bunks in the lower deck and Robert and Paul were near each other in their bunks. Their gear was placed in a foot locker at the foot of their beds, and Robert went over to investigate the rest of the ship.

"Are you going to be O.K. Crook?" Robert asked, knowing the remorse Paul was feeling as they were about to set sail.

"Yes." Paul replied. "I think I will just stay here for now, I feel tired, and I just want to lie on my bunk for awhile." Robert left Paul to himself thinking it might do Paul some good just to be alone for awhile till he got used to the idea that he was no longer in Europe, that he would be home in a week or so.

There were other men who came down the isle of the bunks who were getting situated with their sleeping arrangements. They were loud and in good spirits, for they were happy to be going home. They were yelling at each other and cutting up with their friends. Paul did not feel this way at all, and he just turned his back to them, and was just lying there until they left to go to the chow hall. Then he was alone, and he could think to himself. He was miserable, and he felt every inch of misery as he lay there and pondered about what to do about the situation he was in. He knew he had to go back to the States, and away from here, but his heart and his head couldn't agree what to do about the fact that he didn't want to go home just yet. He could imagine Anna there in

Fahrenzhausen waiting patiently for him to return, and when would it be that he would be able to return to this foreign land? He had no idea, and the fear of leaving her haunted him for the rest of the trip.

The ship arrived back in the United States on June 2nd. They were home, and it should have been a happy time for both of the men. Paul had been seasick for most of the trip. Robert was glad he was back and his girlfriend met him at the docks. Paul could see why Robert never got involved with any of the German women because Robert's girlfriend was very beautiful. He was happy for Robert to be seeing the one he loved again.

They reported to Fort Bragg late that day and on June 6th both were stunned when they were given their discharge papers. They were free to go home with no obligation to the Army again. The war was over and they were free to live their own lives again, but only in America.

11
Back to Ramhurst in the Aftermath of the War

The bus ride home took a day and a half. The bus had made so many stops that Paul got confused about where they were. When the bus finally arrived in Chatsworth, Georgia, Paul had to wait an hour and a half before he could catch a ride down Old Ramhurst Road to the farm house. He got out at the driveway, which was far from the house, walked down the long drive. As he neared the house, he got his first look at the farm house. Tar paper roof, old siding and no porch, blocks for steps. Not much to it, but it was home now, and it would just have to do.

Charles was out in the yard and he had to blink twice when he saw a soldier coming down the drive, to see that it was his brother Paul. He ran immediately into the house calling for his mother. Adell, Mary and William all came running, screaming and ran to meet him coming to the house. They were so very glad to see that Paul was home. When he told them that he was discharged from the Army, they screamed for joy again because they knew the nightmare of him being gone away was over.

"You are so thin!" his mother exclaimed. "I'm going to have to do some good cooking to fatten you up."

Indeed Paul had been overweight a bit before going to Germany, and almost a boy of only nineteen, but now he had come back thin and much wiser than his years. He had become a man while he was gone overseas.

It was already late in the day and was Paul was so tired from riding the bus so far. Paul was eager to get into civilian clothes before dinner, and when he put his old clothes on, he realized then just how much weight he had really lost.

"Charlie, I think I might have to borrow some of your clothes," he remarked as he showed Charles how his clothes hung on him.

"My Gosh, you have lost a lot of weight, Paul!" his brother exclaimed, as he reached inside the clothes cabinet and pulled out some clothes of his own for Paul.

Dinner was served, and they all sat around the table and for once in two years they were all together once again. Adell said prayer before eating, and thanked God for bringing her son back home to them.

"It seems strange, you sitting here at the table with us after all this time," Adell remarked. Paul felt almost out of place for this kitchen was different from where they lived before; but he looked up to see that big smile on his mother's face, and he knew that he was home.

"It seems strange to be in civilian clothes again after two years too, Mother," he replied.

"But you look so good." Mary said, "Your weight loss suits you. I have never seen you look more handsome." Paul blushed, and lowered his eyes on his food. He was embarrassed.

"Now now," Adell started, "He's much too thin and will need to gain a little weight to look like himself."

Paul told them bits about his adventures, about how he had to sleep in a barn or two when out on patrol, and how that his unit dug holes in the snow banks, and the dirt to sleep just to keep from freezing to death from the elements. He talked about the difference between the Nazis and the common people in Germany, but didn't say a word about Anna and the Reinoehls. It was a raw sore with him that he was now home, and he was happy for the chance to be here for he dreamed about it for so long. But now Fahrenzhausen was a world away and there in Fahrenzhausen was Anna, the love he had had to leave behind.

That night he slept on the couch; Charles and William shared a small bedroom, and Adell and Mary slept in the other. The house was only a four-room house, with two bedrooms, a kitchen and a small living area. The out-house was far in the woods, behind the house and everything here seemed small.

Adell, Paul's mother, got him some clean sheets to put on the sofa, which was old and rickety and all worn; she wanted him to feel clean, and the crisp new sheets were as clean as he was going to get on that make-shift bed. He almost felt like a guest, she was waiting on him so, and it made Paul uncomfortable. This didn't feel like home. As he lay on the couch late into the night, everything hit him at once. How would he ever get back to Fahrenzhausen and how could he afford to go there when there was so much that needed to be done here? These feelings were so overwhelming that he actually felt as sick as he had on the ship, but now he was home and he couldn't blame this current ill feeling on sea-sickness.

Somewhere in Germany

The next few days, Paul spent a lot of time looking around the farm. Adell had spent all the money he had sent home plus all the money she could scrape up herself to buy this house and the land so that they could have a permanent home and would not have to move from place to place. Adell had meant well, thinking only of the future of her children, but the house lacked enough room and what there was of it was in very poor shape. Adell was broke once again thanks to the purchase of the farm. The land was covered with trees and brush and would have to be cleared over time so they could plant gardens. There was some space that was clear just behind the house and over the rise that Adell and her children had already planted with potatoes, corn, okra, beans, squash and tomatoes. Those were the most important vegetables that needed to be planted to make their food to survive, but they needed more, so they could can the food, so that it would last them through the winter until next spring, till planting time came again. There were a few chickens running loose that survived off of what they could peck out of the ground but they needed hogs, and they would have to build pens, and they needed laying hens, and pens would have to be built for them as well, so they could lay eggs and they could trade them with the rolling store for things like flour, sugar, salt and coffee.

Immediately Paul decided he would have to find work and maybe Charles could work with him so they could earn enough money to do some of the things that needed to be done here. Not that Charles and the rest of the family hadn't done the best that they knew how to do, but Paul, as the head of the family after their father had died and after Simon had died, had always been the planner for how much and what they needed to get by. They had done well while he was gone overseas, but now his military pay would not be coming in like before and they would have to live off of what they could make themselves. He did sign up for he Army reserves just before leaving Fort Bragg, and that would provide him a small paycheck monthly from the military; but it would be just that, a small amount.

This feeling was so overwhelming that he went for a walk just to think. He was not very familiar with the property, but he found a high hill in which the there was a warm breeze blowing and he sat down on a tree trunk, where a tree had fallen. He felt completely alone for the first time in his life and tears became heavy in his eyes. His thoughts of Anna and how very far away she was, was a burden on his heart. His heart broke with how much he missed her. He imagined her young face before him and thought about how lovely she was and about how she made him laugh with her gestures. He asked God to help him cope with his sadness and to deliver him from the misery he was feeling at this moment. He was alone, so he felt free to let his tears flow, but he knew crying about feeling overwhelmed, and missing Anna, was not going to help matters. After he sat and thought for such a long time, he got up and walked back towards the farmhouse. He had to get a hold of himself and not let his mother or sister and brothers see just how miserable he was. It was time to put aside his thoughts and get back to the reality of what responsibilities lay before him.

Paul got a job at the thread mill in Dalton which made him very happy to have a paycheck coming in to the family. His employer sent a bus to Ramhurst every morning to pick up workers to work there in the thread mill. He was happy to have a job and tried to get Charles on there at the plant but they had no job for

Charles at that time. His supervisor told him that when work picked up, that maybe they could hire Charles also. When the bus brought them home late in the day, he would eat supper and then go work in the fields. There was land to clear, so there were trees to cut down, so that they could have more fields in which to plant on, chopping weeds, picking vegetables for his mother and the others to put up the next day while he was at work. They had apple trees and his mother and Mary had been peeling apples, cutting them up and laying them out in the sun on white cloths for them to dry. This would be a good fruit that Adell could make fried apple pies and other things with in the winter. They were glad to have the apple trees.

Summer was hot, and time seemed to fly with all his new responsibilities, with the thread mill and the gardening. Charles had gotten a part time job at a saw mill up the road; that brought in extra money as well. The gardening proved to be hard because the men only had the evenings to do all the heavy work, and unless you lived in poverty before and knew you basically had to live off the land, you could not understand the enormous amount of work it took to clear land and get it ready for gardening. Trees and brush made the land poor, so the turning of a plow was always necessary to make the soil rich again, suitable for planting. They had to borrow a relative's mule and plow to turn the soil, and it was back-breaking work that could put you into an early grave if you were not healthy to begin with.

The property they had cleared was ready and they planted a late garden to bring in more vegetables that they might trade at the market or with the rolling store. This year the weather had been right for replanting, but every year was not the same. They had been lucky this year, when the temperatures had been right to make a fall harvest possible.

Time was so short now, that Paul would fall into the couch late at night exhausted and go into a deep sleep. He knew something had to be done soon about the space in the house, and he was saving every penny he could.

12
Letters from Anna

On August 6th a letter from Germany arrived at the farmhouse. Adell had received it from the postman and put it on the table for Paul. She was sure it would be the talk of the town that Paul received this letter, for it was all the way from Germany, and no one, no one got a letter from overseas in this area. It was addressed to Paul Crook, Rt.1, Romhurst, Georgia U.S.A. Adell didn't say anything about it, but Mary immediately told Paul when he came in from work that he had a letter and he went and looked at it.

"You've got a letter all the way from Germany!" Mary exclaimed, excited that a letter had came from so far away. "Who is it from?"

"It's from the Reinoehl Family," Paul replied as he looked at the letter. The familiar name was on the return address, he could see that the letter was from Anna. He was very eager to look at it closer. He could see that Mary was curious about the letter; he carried it into the back bedroom and looked at it closer in private. It was from Anna Reinoehl, dated July 17th, 1946. It was written in German, so he could not read it; evidently Anna could not write in English, even with the English lessons, but a smile came across his face as he could feel Anna thinking of him, longing for him. He suddenly felt the warmth of the love that he had felt in Fahrenzhausen as he held Anna in his arms. Oh God, how he missed her! All he knew was that at the bottom, it said, "Goodbye, Von Anna, Mama, Papa" in English. He looked at the letter in his hand, and felt the paper between his fingers and examined the writing. It felt good to hold something in his hands that had also been in Anna's hands.

The others asked him about the letter at supper and he told them it was from Anna and the Reinoehl family in Fahrenzhausen, Germany. He told them that he had spent time with the Reinoehl's and that they were good to him. That seemed to satisfy their curiosity and they asked him no more questions about the letter. He didn't tell them that he and Anna had been in love, and that he thought about her every day. Paul was such a personal man, and what had been between him and Anna was just that—personal.

Late that night, before he went to sleep, he wondered what she was saying in the letter. He looked at the letter again, before He put the letter in an old hat box of his mother's on top of the shelf robe for safe keeping. If he could find someone who knew German, then maybe he could get them to read it to him. But, there were no Germans in this part of the country, so he would never know what this letter said. All he knew was that it was from Anna. It made him wonder what she was thinking of him, wondering if she knew for a fact that he was in the States. He wondered if she was waiting on him and he felt like he wanted to go back there as soon as possible.

Americans disliked the German people because of the war. Adell had mentioned her dislike for the Germans on more than one occasion. Paul would try to explain that all Germans were not bad people, in fact, there were a lot of good people who were Germans; but she would just scold him and then he would not say anything more.

Adell had been thinking about the letter from Germany. Paul had not been home for very long, and she wondered what the letter was about. Adell only wanted the best for her children, but she also never wanted them to leave her. Why was this Anna Reinoehl and her family writing to Paul?

Early in November, there was another letter from Anna. It was dated October 21st, 1946. It too was in German and again Paul could not understand what it contained, except that at the end it said, "Anna, and familie." Paul was frustrated wishing he knew what Anna was trying to communicate in her letters. He noticed that both letters had been censored by the Civil Censorship, but nothing had been blacked out, so she had only included what would get through the censorship board. Was she still waiting for him? Thoughts like these made him want to go there as quickly as possible. If only he could.

Another letter came in early December dated November 17, 1946. Again, it was in German, and although it said "Lieber Paul," at the beginning—and he knew that meant "Dear Paul"—he could not understand the contents of the letter except at the end where it read "Anna, and family, Papa, Mama and Niklas."

This was the third letter that had come to the farmhouse and although he thought about writing back to her, she could not read English and he could not write German, and in the end he did not write. He put the third letter in the same hatbox that belonged to his mother for safe keeping.

Then the letters stopped.

At Christmas he thought so very much of Anna and the Reinoehl family and wondered if Anna still wore the heart necklace that he had given her on the night that he first told her that he loved her. He wondered if Mrs. Reinoehl used her present that he had given her during the days of their Christmas holidays. He even wondered if little Niklas got treats or twigs in his boot this year. He regretted not being able to there this year at Christmas to make their holiday as special as he had last year. He doubted that they would have a suckling pig for their meal. It had been so long now that he had been in Fahrenzhausen, it made his heart heavy thinking that Anna could have forgotten all about him by now.

But no, Anna had not forgotten him, for she had sent the letters to show she was still thinking of him; and he was thinking about her, too, even though the miles between them were many. After they built on to this house, he would start saving for the fare to go to Germany before it was too late. He did not know how much the fare would be, but he would start saving nevertheless.

The next spring, towards the first of March, Charles and Paul started the renovation of the farmhouse. They laid the block, and Charles bought lumber at a discount from the mill. Roofing and siding was expensive and the interior of the house would have to be finished too. It was costing much more money than they had planned for. The kitchen was not complete until late that year.

Another year had passed and Paul was busy farming in the summer and working on the side. He had not been able to save any money with the cost of the construction on the house. But he vowed that he would start to save for the fare to Fahrenzhausen as soon as possible. Another Christmas went by and again he wondered about Anna and the Reinoehl Family.

There were times when Paul would be working in the garden and he would get so angry, tired of all the work and responsibility that he would get frustrated and instead of chopping weeds, he would chop down the plants. Once he even threw down his hoe with anguish and marched toward the house, ready to tell his mother that he was going back to Germany.

Would Anna still be waiting for him, he wondered? What if she found someone else? It had been over a year since her last letter and she had probably gone on with her life. Paul suddenly felt sorrow instead of anguish; instead of going to the house to tell his mother he was going to Germany, he turned and went and sat on the high hill where the wind always blew to get over these feelings. He cried at the love he had lost. It was not Adell's fault or his family's. They had just relied on him as they always did and they didn't know that he was longing for a woman all those miles away. It was not their fault, it was his, and he just couldn't—wouldn't—take it out on them.

The renovations on the farmhouse had been finished and it looked finally like a house instead of a shack. They were all proud of the way the renovations had gone; now it felt like a decent home for the Crook family. They had built a new kitchen and dining area, added a new living room and converted the old living room to a bedroom where Paul now slept. It was still a bit crowded for five people but was so much better than before.

Life was filled with work and Mary and Adell and Charles had all gotten jobs at McCartey Chenille in Dalton. Charles bought an old car, and Paul got an old Ford truck for the farm and it finally looked like Paul could save some money. He had inquired about how much a boat trip would be across the ocean; if he brought Anna back with him, it would be double the fare coming back. He kept wondering if she wanted to come with him. Would it be fair of him to take her away from her family? With that kind of money for the fare, there would be no trips back. It would take him a long time to come up with the money he was sure.

In late November of 1948, another letter came to the farm house. Again it was from Anna.

Paul Crook
Rt. 1
Romhurst, Ga U.S.A

The return address it read:

Miss Anna Reinoehl
Braumeister 26
Fahrenzhausen, München Germany

Paul noticed it said "Miss," which meant that Anna was not yet married. Also he noticed that the Civil Censorship didn't have their stamp on it. That didn't mean that they hadn't censored it, but he could not see the stamp. He knew they still had troops there in Germany, but he wondered if there, they still stood post at Fahrenzhausen.

Again it ended, "Anna, Mama, Papa, and Niklas." She thought of him! and it added fuel to the flame, igniting a new fire in Paul's belly. He promised himself that he would have the money in about six months.

Adell asked Paul why these people kept writing to him. Paul explained to her that they were really good to him and someday he wished they could come here to the farm. That infuriated Adell, and she declared that under no circumstances would Germans would ever set foot in her house.

Paul's mothers words shocked him. To think she would judge someone without even knowing what he or she was like—even someone innocent as Anna. Paul fought back and forth in his mind about how his mother felt about Germans. If he brought Anna here, they wouldn't be able to live in this house, that was plain. That meant he would have to save more money to provide Anna a home.

Adell's brother—Paul's uncle—had always had a bad habit of gambling. He would go to Detroit and gamble all of his money on horse races and come home broke. He had many children and a wife and the family was constantly bailing him out. This year was no different.

In March of 1949 the family received a telegram from Detroit. Adell's brother was in jail and someone from the family would have to come and pay his bail. No one ever really explained what crime was committed but Paul was sure that it had something to do with gambling. Maybe he had gotten into trouble with a bookie or the mafia. No one in the family had this kind of money to go to Detroit and pay his way out of jail, except Paul. They all knew Paul rarely spent money on himself, and they knew he banked over in Dalton and kept quiet about how much money he had in his account. Adell begged Paul for the money; this was her baby brother, and Paul's, only uncle, even though he had been gone from the family for along time now.

Paul reluctantly went to the bank, withdrew his money and went to Detroit. In the process, he lost his job because he was not able to show up for work, for this trip took over a week there and back. When Paul returned a week later, his uncle with him, nothing was said about why his uncle had been in jail and how much it cost to get him out of trouble. But, once again, Paul was broke. Another crisis, another delay and the money he had saved to go back to Germany was gone.

In 1951, Paul decided too much time had passed for him ever to think about going back to Fahrenzhausen. It saddened him, for it had been five years since he had left there and three years since he had gotten Anna's last letter. She had gone on with her life by now, he was sure. She had forgotten about him.

It was time for him to give up on the idea of Anna…of going back to Germany and to Anna. He had been young then when he was in that strange land, and foolish to think he and Anna could have ever had a future, but when he was there in Fahrenzhausen, he had been so in love that he was blind to the differences in their lives.

Paul could never know how hard it would be getting past these old feelings, and putting it all behind him. He could think about her, no one could ever take away his thoughts of her, no matter how much they might try. And he could dream about her which he did from time to time; no matter how much he would try not to, he could not tell his unconscious mind not to dream about her. When he would awake, he would be glad that he had dreamed about her, but it would frustrate him even more knowing he would never be able to have her, and hold her, and love her as he had wanted so dearly to. Paul loved her still with a deep, abiding love. But he had his work, he had his farming, and he had his memories, and that would just have to be enough.

13
The Later Years

*M*ary had gotten married in 1951 and had a son in 1952. Paul loved this child from the time he was just a baby, and as the child grew, Paul was always a good uncle. He and his nephew spent so much time together that Paul began to think of him as a son. They gardened together and any where Paul was, David, his nephew, was right behind him. As David grew into a young man, Paul wished he could have been his son. I married Mary's son David in 1976 and became part of Paul's family.

William left home and married and the farmhouse suddenly seemed much bigger. Now Paul, Charles, and Adell each had a bedroom and there was plenty of room in what once seemed a small house. Paul slept in the back bedroom and among his things was his mother's old hatbox, where he kept Anna's letters and his medals that he never showed anyone. He had his memories and sometimes late at night, he would recall those memories as if it was yesterday, just for a few moments, just before he would fall asleep and dream about Fahrenzhausen.

When I came into the family, I immediately fell in love with both Uncle Charles and Uncle Paul. The family was very close-knit, and their very being existed by being around each other, and always considering each other.

I knew Paul personally for twenty-five years and had gone many times to that old saltbox house in Tails Creek where they had lived as children. Mary told us it was haunted for they heard knocking in the walls late at night.

David and I went to the farmhouse at Ramhurst almost every Sunday all those years, especially so after Adell died in 1982. David and I had three sons and Paul and Charles loved to spoil them. Our children spent a lot of time with the both of them, staying at the farm on weekends and during the summers when school was out. I felt close to Charles, Mary and Paul and had heard the stories of 1935 when their father had died and about how meager that Christmas had been.

Paul never talked about Anna after 1948, never told David or me about Anna or that he had been in love during the war when he was posted in Fahrenzhausen. Charles and Mary remembered the letters coming to the house so many years ago, but that had been so long ago that all of that had been forgotten about, except for Paul.

I'm sure he thought about Anna from time to time over the years. Following the war, Paul never dated, never married, never had children. He just worked and farmed, plowing the land with his tractor, growing hay and bailing it. We always thought of him as a driven man, for even in the later years, he worked nights as a security guard. During the day, he would be at home. Sometimes in the summer when David was a little boy, Uncle Paul would come on the tractor, pick David up, and take him to the field. A creek flowed beside one of the lower fields, and when it was hot they would swim after a hard day's work. Charles would join them, swimming with David, as Paul sat on the bank to rest. Paul worked like a mule and you would hardly ever see him unless you went to the fields and found his old truck; you would know that he was there somewhere on the tractor, plowing or taking care of something. Paul had an old 8N Ford tractor that he had for years, and later when he was much older, he just bought another newer version of the same tractor. After David and I married, sometimes we would get behind him as he drove the tractor down the road on the way to the fields. David would tell me about the trips to the field as a child, and he would always say what a hard worker Uncle Paul had been. No one knew of the love he had had for Anna, or why he tried to fill up his time with work. He did not want to be an idle person, with time to sit around and think about all he had lost. He had made a choice many years ago, he had lived with it for years now, and he would do so for the rest of his life. He was an avid farmer, and bought a lot of farm equipment for the farm, tractors, a combine, hay bailers. He was a modern farmer but with an old-fashioned heart that had to start filling its time up with something other than memories.

14
The Farm

*P*aul died in June of 2001. Just two months later, that same year, Charles had a tragic accident. Charles had been retired for a while, and he had kept up the farm as best as he could. He kept baling hay and selling it to local farmers for their horses. When someone close would call for a hay order, he would try to deliver if possible. He was out delivering hay one day to a man who evidently didn't feed his horses enough. When Charles and his nephew Mike arrived to deliver the hay, the hungry horses stampeded the truck. When the truck backed in to unload, Mike got out, and the horse immediately reared up and tried to attack him with his front hooves. Charles ran to Mike's rescue, dashing around the truck to shoo away the horses with his straw hat. Instead of becoming scared and turning way, the horse turned on Charles and trampled him. Charles had several broken bones. His hip was broken severely and they called the ambulance to take him to the hospital. You could see the hooves marks on his chest and ribs.

Somewhere in Germany

After having surgery to repair the hip, Charles had a long stay at the hospital, then began rehab for about three or four weeks. When they got ready to release him, he was told that he would have to go to an assisted living facility unless someone could move in and take care of him. Charles cried and said he didn't want to live in the rehab facility that he wanted to go home. David and I talked it over and we decided to move in for a while and take care of Charles. We lived with him for seven months till he was back on the mend.

Charles had purchased a home below the old farmhouse from his sister Mary in 1977. She and her husband had built a new home just next to the old farmhouse. Their new house had enough room for all of us to stay. It also provided better accessibility for Charles who had to use a walker to help him maneuver around with as he continued his rehab. That left the old farmhouse empty. Though it was full of memories, Paul's absence made it seem sad.

Next spring David and I moved back home to Rocky Face while Charles and Mike continued to live in the big house. It was much newer and more convenient, and it just made better sense for them to stay there. Now the old farmhouse was permanently empty but insurance regulations required someone to live in the old farmhouse for it to be insurable. So Charles decided that he would rent the old farmhouse out to someone; even though it was an old house, he wanted to insure it. It was still full of furniture and personal items left by the family, so some of it had to be moved. The place that was dry and out of the weather was the garage, with the attached storage area. It had a door and was lockable so that all the old stuff would be safe. They moved all of Paul's old papers, watches, land deeds, and personal effects into the storage shed. Even Adell still had things left in her old bedroom, so they moved all of that in there as well. They didn't want to get rid of all her things except her clothing because she was their mother, and they just couldn't bear to part with all of it. The new renters were able to use all the furniture in the house, solving the problem of having to find a place for it as well. Belongings were packed in boxes without really sorting through them. There were still shirts in packages that people had given Paul for Christmas and birthdays. The pins in the shirts had rusted, they had been there for so long.

The renters moved in and lived there for maybe a year or so, then they moved out. New renters moved in and out about six months later. A third renter lived there for a year and it was while they were living there that I finally decided to unlock the garage and look for some old family pictures. The family had not forgotten about Paul's and Adell's belongings, but no one had ever gotten around to sorting through their old things. I was actually looking for a rare picture of Jim Crook, Adell's husband who had died in 1935. I hadn't seen the old photograph in so long that I wondered what had happened to it. Charles said there might be some things of their father's in the old shed. It took me a while to get around to looking for any evidence of life from Jim Crook, but eventually my zeal for any information about him and his history won out.

I went over to Chatsworth one Sunday just before church let out. Mary said she would like to go thru the old stuff too, but I arrived quite a bit earlier than she did. I let myself in through the now rotting door of the enclosed storage garage and looked around at the mess. Charles was always generous in trying to help people and he had told me to help myself to anything that I might find. I do not feel good about taking other people's things without permission, so I told him that I would bring the items home with me and return them back later. I had boxes and boxes with me and as I sat down and looked through the things in that building, I was overwhelmed with the enormous task of sorting through everything that was there. I don't think that a single document that was ever in Paul's or Adell's possession had been thrown out. I found tons of picture albums Charles had not gotten around to carrying over to the big house, but they certainly did not belong in this musty smelling and damp storage shed! I threw the things that interested me into the boxes, piling things into boxes, hoping to have time when I got home to go through some of it. When Mary finally got out of church, she came over and we went through more things. We even found clippers that her mother and dad had used when they had sewn bedspreads for money in 1933 up until Jim died. Mary remembered that he was reaching up on the mantle to get these clippers when he fell over with a heart attack. Mary had only been five years old at the time but could remember his death all too vividly.

We spent hours in that shed that day, looking through the things that time—and even Charles and Mary—had forgotten. As we sorted through some of Adell's things, Mary would tell me tales of what happened at different times in their lives, and what related to each thing. The old icebox was sitting in a corner and she told me that her and her husband had set up house and that was their first refrigerator. There was an antique television in another corner, one that Charles had bought when they first had got a TV, and then he became so fascinated with how televisions worked that he took a home repair course, and then began repairing televisions for a living. Late evening I realized just how many hours had passed that we had sorted and looked through, and assorted things that I didn't take. I finally told her I needed to start home and so I lugged the boxes out to my car, and placed them in the trunk so that they wouldn't turn over. All told there were about ten boxes. I had enjoyed this day as I always do when its something about history, but especially this day spending time with Mary and her telling me about their life when they were young kids.

When I got home, I unloaded the boxes and placed them into a corner in my bedroom, out of the way and it didn't matter how long they would stay there. I knew it would take me some time to go through it all, so I decided to just take my time. Between working and keeping up my own home, I didn't always have a lot of time for other things, and I knew it would really take some time to go through all of the things I had brought home. Still, I was anxious to look at some of the things I had noticed when loading them into the boxes.

Later that night I did decide to look through a few things, starting with a box that had one of Adell's old pocketbooks in it. I carried it into the living room and sat with David on the couch, for this was his family's things and I wanted him to share with me what we found. An old navy blue purse with a clasp at the top stood out in my mind: in it were letters from Paul during World War II, when he had been overseas in Germany.

Adell had received these letters in 1945 and 1946 and there were about twenty-one of them. They best way for me to read them, I decided, was to put them in order and take them out one at a time. That way I could read them in the order as to the way he had written them and I was sure these would be fascinating and hold a lot of information about what he had experienced in Germany. These letters were almost fifty-nine years old and I had to handle them carefully. The first one I read said:

> *Somewhere in Germany*
> *Dear Mother,*
>
> *I hope this letter finds you doing well. How are the gardens? I suppose you are planting things now as it is spring there. Are Charles, Mary, and William doing O.K.? I hope so. Tell them I said hello, and I am thinking of all of you. I guess they are working hard around the farm. Tell Mary and William to learn as much as they can in school.*
>
> *I love you mother,*
> *Love,*
> *Paul*

The letter was simple, basic, not saying much at all. I wondered about that. The next letter was the same, repeating the same thing, over and over again. Each letter I read made me wonder why he didn't say more about what he was doing in Germany. Later I realized that the letters were being censored by the U.S. Civil Censorship Service and the soldiers were told by the military not to write about anything they were doing or where they were located or anything of the sort. The thing that amazed me about the letters was that they were in such good shape. They looked like they had been put in the purse just yesterday. Adell had put these letters all in one purse and if someone had thrown this purse out, the letters would have been gone. I put them aside after reading them all, but kept them for a further look later.

That had been the most fascinating thing thus far that I had found. I kept looking in the days that followed and went through and photocopied pictures and documents. Paul's official war records were in there as well. He had won the Bronze Star Medal of Honor while he was in Germany and his award papers were in with his Official War records. I had heard the story before, about how he had killed fifteen Germans, wounded one and captured twenty-four—all by himself. But seeing this document brought it home to me. I remembered my husband telling me that he never talked about what he had done to win the Bronze Star, and that he even never told the family about it. It wasn't until a magazine came to the house that next year after he was discharged from the Army that they even knew anything about it. In that magazine was an article about what Paul had done as a soldier in Germany. Paul had never told anyone about the medal, and he never discussed what had happened in the battle of Appenrode.

Paul was ashamed of taking human life, when his mother had always raised her children to believe that killing was wrong, and a sin, and that you would be punished in the after life for sinning. He didn't feel like a hero, and he didn't want to be praised for what he considered a sin.

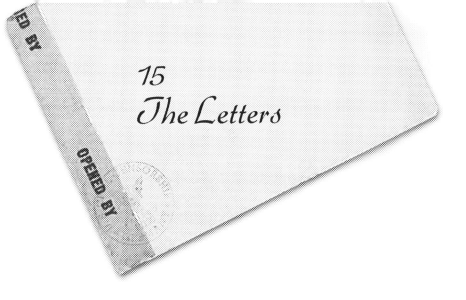

15
The Letters

*A*s I went through all the boxes, one by one, I put aside the things that looked important enough to warrant further investigation, pictures I wanted to copy for my work on our family history, and documents that I wanted to read again. Some of these things were fascinating to me for some of these documents were sixty years old or older. I even found a paper that Jim Crook had written and signed before his death in 1935.

So many of these documents were really old and I had trouble believing that they still existed, as old as they were. I think the Crook family must have saved every piece of paper that they had ever had, because there was so much that I had to work my way through, and it really took a long time.

Inside one of those cartons was a little wooden box. I remember thinking that I would take a look at it later. The intricate carvings on the outside made me think it was a jewelry box. When I opened it, inside I found four letters. I realized they were written in German and I couldn't read them. The only thing I could read was the address to Paul Crook, and the return address of Anna Reinoehl. Paul was the only one who had been to Germany, so of course they were his, but who was this Anna? I put the letters on a shelf in my computer desk and thought little about them until later when I asked my mother-in-law, Mary if she remembered someone by the name of Anna Reinoehl and told her about the letters. She told me that Paul had known some people by the name of Reinoehl but she couldn't remember much about 1946, when they letters had been delivered to the farm.

The letters stayed on that shelf for months, untouched, and unnoticed, but ever so present in my home. I went through all the other family things, and boxed them up again after I had copied all that I wanted to save. I believe in giving people their things back, so a month or so later, David and I carried the boxes back to give back to Charles. I carried them down to the big house and told Charles that they didn't belong in the garage, because there was a lot of important stuff in there. He agreed with me, and we found a place for them in a closet in the dining room.

The letters remained in my home, still sitting quietly on the shelf of my computer desk. I would walk by, see them sitting there sticking out from the rest of the clutter, and I would think to myself, that I needed to find out about those letters. Then I would forget about them again. The letters started talking to me, for when I would see them, I would listen to my conscience telling me that I needed to get them translated. It was as if they were speaking to me, saying, *here I am, find out about me, I am harboring a secret, something no one knows about*. Still, I continued to ignore the letters because I didn't know anyone at the time that could speak or read German.

Almost a year went by. One day I was cleaning some of the clutter off of my computer desk and ran across the letters on the shelf where I had left them. I looked at them again, yellowed, aged from time, bearing foreign postal stamps on the front. Also on the front was a stamp that said "Censored by Civil Service." On the edge, someone had opened the letter and retaped it. The tape read, "opened by," then the stamp was stamped near the tape not to interfere with the address of the person it was addressed to.

I took the letters with me into the kitchen, sat down and looked at each, one at a time. I noticed the dates and they started out with "Lieber Paul," which I assumed meant "Dear Paul." Later that night I told David I really would like to know what was in those letters.

I made a mental note to try to find someone who could read them to me. One week, we were camping at the lake. It is the place we go to relax and where David likes to fish. This time, we met a Swiss man and his American wife. He had come to the United States to work as an engineer years ago, met and married his wife and stayed on. Our campground is usually crowded with people— about 70 campers—and because of the mild weather, we go year 'round. The winter is quiet and we just go to relax, because fishing isn't at its peak then. Summer, on the other hand, is an exciting time for there are a lot of people around, and we enjoy socializing with some of them. I asked the Swiss man if he could read and speak German. I told him about my uncle's letters that were in German and that we could not read. He said he could read German and would be glad to read them to us if we would bring them sometime when he was there.

The week of the July 4, 2006, I carried the letters to the lake, hoping to run into the Swiss man and his wife. Our son Jason joined us with his family, and we had a lot of fun with our boat and being on the water. We even got to watch the fireworks on the from the water with friends from Birmingham.

I saw the Swiss man later in the week and asked him when would be a good time for him to read the letters. He said that he would read them then, if I would go and get them. I returned soon afterward with David, and Jason and the letters. We sat around a big outdoor table with the Swiss man and his wife. There was an air of anticipation as he began to read. The letters, we realized, were love letters written to Paul from this German girl. He read each letter slowly; they were almost the same, yet each a little different in its own way. Suddenly we felt in awe of the fact that these love letters were to Paul, and it felt like we had stumbled onto something so personal, that we shouldn't be reading it. We had known Paul for many years—David had known him his whole life—and we knew that he never married, or dated for all we knew, so this German girl writing these love letters to him was kind of shocking to us. It almost felt as if we were invading his privacy but since he had been dead for five years, I guess it was O.K. Though it was 98 degrees outside, I began to get cold chills through my body. We never knew Paul to have anybody other than family and it suddenly felt good to know that someone special had really loved him.

In each Anna professed her love for Paul, talking about the time when they had been in love and he had to quickly leave for England. She kept asking for him to send her a picture of himself. That's all I could remember as the Swiss man read, and I was sure there had been more but I would have to wait till I could get them translated because I did not want to take any more time away from his vacation. I would wait to hear everything that they said, and I would have to find someone who could translate.

Hearing the letters brought up a lot of questions: Who was Anna Reinoehl? How did they meet? Paul must have been in love with her too, because he kept her letters in his bedroom for fifty-five years until the day he died! And to think I had found those letters in a hovel, tucked away in an old enclosed garage.

We sat there for a long time and talked about these letters after the Swiss man read them to us. I made the comment that I wondered if Anna could possibly still be alive. If she had been eighteen in 1946, then she would be seventy-eight now, if she were still alive.

The Swiss man told us that most German people didn't move around much and that they lived in the same place for years. He suggested that I write to that sixty-year-old address, and that she could possibly still live in that very house. The likelihood of Anna still being alive seemed to me to be pretty far-fetched and I wasn't sure the Swiss man knew what he was talking about. But he *was* a world traveler and might know about these things, so I decided it was worth a try.

My brother was a soldier in Iraq at that time, and my sister-in-law and I spoke quite often. I told her about the letters and she said a lady that went to church with her was German and she would ask her if she could translate the letters for me. The lady agreed. She translated the first one and told us that it was filled with grief and sadness for a love lost.

The first letter touched my sister-in-law so much that she told me that if I wrote to Anna, to please, please send her a picture of Paul, since she kept begging for one. The first letter said:

Somewhere in Germany

Fahrenzhausen, München
Deutschland, July 17, 1946
Dear Paul,

You promised that you would come back to me.

Was that goodbye? The goodbye from you was very hard for me. You was always so pleasant and lovely to me. You told me that you had to go to London, and then you would come back. I waited mornings and night. Now I am thinking you went to_____?

Dear Paul,

You promised me a pretty picture. Please send it to me. I would like to look at your picture, when I know I can't see you in person.

Dear Paul,

The days was so nice when you was here. My parents loved you too. Oh when I think on that morning when I gave you a trichein [is like a scarf]. For the goodbyes you looked at me so lovely and nice and we could not get apart.

Dear Paul,

I would like to see you one more time. I wish I could come to you but my wish would not come true. I cried a lot. You was gone so fast. You knew that my heart was with you. Now I am alone and unhappy till I get a letter again.

I had a friend, till the Americans came. Why was I so young, so many Americans coming back for the girl's. Just me waiting till you come back.

Dear Paul,
*   Are you still sometimes think about us?*
*   We have so much work in the garden.*
Goodbye, wish you the best
Von Anna, Mama and Papa
Please write back soon, and send me a picture.

How lovely and sad, the words plucked right out of World War II and its aftermath. I was mortified at the thought this young woman grieved the loss of their love so. I could not imagine what she was feeling while she wrote this letter, she seemed almost desperate to hear from him, and I suppose she was, for love knows no boundaries, and though she assumed he was back in the United States, her love for him was so strong it could cross oceans.

This letter stayed with me for days, weeks and touched my very soul. Again I had so many unanswered questions, questions that I might never get answers for, because without Anna and Paul in front of me how would I ever know? Paul had died, and as for Anna, I had no idea if she was still living or she had died also; I would never get answers. Again, I asked Mary about the letters from Anna, and again she said she just remembered them coming to the farmhouse after Paul came back from Germany. But I had to keep reminding myself that Paul could not read German so he didn't know what she was saying and that she sounded so desperate, and that she still professed to love him.

16
Love Knows No Boundaries

*I*t took me awhile to get the other letters translated, because I did not want my sister-in-law's friend to be overwhelmed, so I found another person who I had known for years to help me translate the other three letters. She was a person whose husband David had known. I had forgotten about Kitty and the fact that she was German, until she came into my workplace one day. I told her the story about the letters and she happily agreed to translate the others. When she brought them back to me, she said they had almost taken her breath away, they were so sad. She remembered her time in Germany as a young girl, hearing of these stories and how heartbroken some of these women had become when their army men never came back. She said she shared the story with some of her German friends as well, and that it had brought back a lot of memories to them.

The second letter from Anna was written on October 21, 1946—just a few months after she had written the first. It arrived at the farmhouse about two or three weeks later. It said:

Fahrenzhausen, München
Deutschland
October 21, 1946
Dear Paul:
  For the second time I write you dear Paul a letter.
Do you still think about Fahrenzhausen? We welcomed you
with love.
You went with me to English lessons and right when we
were in love, we had to separate. You said you had to go to
England. It was so hard for me. But you promised that you
would come back and you promised me a picture of you.
Until this day, I am still waiting for you. You know I love
you so much. My parents liked you so much too.
  All your fellow soldiers never let anything hear from them.
Greeting and Kisses,
Your Anna and Familie

Again, Anna professed her love for Paul, and again he knew
the letters were from Anna, but he knew not what they said. I am
sure that when he received the letters, he felt good to know she
was thinking of him, and he could feel the love in just that, but
somehow it wasn't enough to overcome the obstacles that he faced
in his life. If only he had known what the letters said.

I tried to imagine what it would feel like to be so in love with
someone so far away, knowing that it would be nearly impossible
to return to them. My heart broke for Paul and Anna, and I
wondered whether either of them dared to think about the
possibility of their separation while they were seeing each other?
I really think Paul thought he would return to Fahrenzhausen

when he completed his duty in England, and I really doubt that he thought for one minute that the army would be sending him home directly from there. I could imagine how his heart would beat when he thought about her, and how depressed he would feel when he feared he might never see her again.

The farm got in the way, I was sure, because he had to pour everything he could into the farmhouse and the farm itself, and I'm sure that at times he wanted to give it all up for Anna, and go back to Germany, but his family meant everything to him too, and it was a choice that he could not make.

The third letter, written on November 17, 1946, arrived at the farmhouse just before Christmas. It probably felt like a Christmas present to Paul knowing that just by receiving this letter, he knew she was thinking of him. And he was thinking of her.

Fahrenzhausen, München
Deutschland Nov.17, 1946
Dear Paul,

Greetings from Fahrenzhausen, from the Reinoehl family. Do you still think about, when you picked me up for my English lessons? It was so nice, we were so happy until we had to say Goodbye. You said with hot kisses—I will come back to you….I waited and you never did come back. You said you had to go to England and I waited until your time there was over, but still you did not come.

I cried day and night. You promised me a picture of you but still to this day, nothing. My parents liked you so very much. They were shocked that you didn't come back. Please, at least send me a picture of you.

Somewhere in Germany

All your fellow soldiers never let anything hear from them.
Please let me hear something from you!

Greetings and until then,
Anna and familie, Papa, Mama and Niklas

The fourth letter was written about two years after the first three.

November 24, 1948
Fahrenzhausen, Germany
Dear Paul!

   I am waiting for such a long time to get a letter from
you. But nothing. Dear Paul, Do you not think about the
goodbye by the garden door. You told me you had to go to
England, and that I would get a pretty picture from you.
But today, still no photo and you did not come back. Dear
Paul, please let me hear from you! Till then, best wishes,

   And love, from Annie, with familie, Papa, and Mama
and Niklas.

   I am waiting on you.
   I promised you that.
   You can write to me in English.

After contemplating the content of the letters, I decided to take the Swiss man's advice. What could it hurt to send a letter to Germany to a sixty-year-old address? My doubts about getting a response were big but I thought there could be a slim chance that he could be right and Anna could possibly live in the same house. I thought long and hard about what I wanted to say to Anna or her relatives, be whoever would receive the letter. I wrote two letters, just alike and sent both even though it was the same address. I thought one could get lost in the mail, but the chance of both of them getting lost probably would not happen. I mailed them late August or September of 2006 and waited for a response.

This is the letter as I sent it:

I am writing this letter to "Anna Reinoehl" if she is still living or to her family if she is deceased. I don't know where to begin my story, but I have been urged by a Swiss man and his wife, who are friends of mine to send this letter to the original address on Anna Reinoehls letters that she wrote to a U.S. Soldier 1946–1948.

Anna wrote 4 letters as far as I know to a man who at the time was a soldier—Private first class—in the United States Army and was stationed in Germany for a year or two. She met him, and they fell in love according to the letters that I have read. The soldier's name was Paul Crook, she wrote to Paul Crook, Romhurst, Georgia U.S.A. The town is now called Chatsworth.

Anna Reinoehl would be in her late 70s or early 80s if she still lives.

Anna, if you, yourself, receive these letters, I just want to tell you about a great love story. I am Paul's niece-in-law. I married Paul's nephew. My name is Debbie King. I want to tell you with deep regret that Paul died about 5 years ago. He was a very decent and wonderful man. I knew him for about 25 years. When Paul was young, about the age of 10 years, his father died and Paul had many siblings, brothers and sisters.

All together there were about 10 of them and Paul was the oldest of the youngest four children. His mother was widowed and poor. The older children left home early through their marriages and the youngest 4 lived with their mother.

Paul was about 18 when he was drafted into the American Army. He knew it was one way that he could help his mother financially. After boot camp, he went to Fort Hood, Texas and was on active duty there before going to Germany. He began sending an allowance out of his pay to his mother to help with the younger children. She saved every penny, and soon had enough money to purchase a small farm in Ramhurst, Georgia. (The town was actually named Ramhurst, but Anna wrote Romhurst on her address to Paul.) The family grew vegetable gardens to feed themselves and raised chickens and pigs. The weather stayed warm here almost all the time. Paul had really helped his mother. His younger brothers, Charles, William, and his younger sister Mary benefited from his being in the Army. They tended to the farm and the gardens, and Paul's mother did the rest. Times were hard, life was hard and at times they almost starved to death.

I know that Paul must have loved you because, after his death, I cleaned out an enclosed garage that had a lot of family belongings in it, and I found letters from Paul to his mother during the war. She had stuck them in a old purse and they had stayed there. And then I came across an old wooden box and that's where I found your letters—or the letters from Anna Reinoehl. Paul had kept your letters all those years and they had been in his bedroom for 55 years *until his death. After he died, the box and all his belongings had been put in the enclosed garage.*

I can't read German, so at first I just looked at the letters and saw the name of Anna Reinoehl, but I just put them away. About a year later I came across the letters again and I wondered who you were and what the letters said. I asked Paul's sister if he ever mentioned you and she did not know anything, or remember. That had been along time ago.

Recently I met a Swiss man and his wife and I found out that he could speak German and read German. I carried the letters to him and he was able to read 3 of the letters and he said that one of them was old German and he could not translate it as well. It was then that I realized that you, Anna had been the only woman Paul had ever loved. Your letters were beautiful but so sad at the same time.

Basically the letters said:

> *Paul,*
>
> *Why have you not written to me or sent me a picture of yourself like you said you would? You promised, remember before you left for England?*
>
> *Are you still thinking of me and what we shared before you left? I have cried every day since you have been gone. We spent so much good times together and Mama and Papa and Niklas love you as well.*
>
> *Please let me hear from you!*
> *Love,*
> *Your Anna Reinoehl*

There probably was more, but that's what I remember the Swiss man reading when he read the letters to us. The letters are in German but Anna was taking English lessons when Paul was getting ready to return to the States and he went with her to the English lessons. Paul came back from the Army, and was discharged with an honorable discharge. He also won a Bronze Star Medal of Honor for Heroism, which was a high honor in the American Army. He had to help raise his brothers and sisters and help his mother. When Anna's letters came to the farmhouse in Romhurst, they were written in German and unfortunately Paul could not read German, and Anna evidently could not write English. Paul did not know what the letters said. He lived in a small southern town and there were no Germans here anywhere around in this area. So, he could not get them translated. He did not know what Anna was saying in her letters.

Because of World War II and the Holocaust, Germans were frowned upon in the United States at that time, in 1946. All people have good in them and Paul saw this in the family of Anna and the Reinoehls. He just didn't know what to do about the situation. I am also sure that if he told the Reinoehls about the Bronze Star and the fact that he killed 15 Germans and captured 24 and wounded one, and that's how he won the bronze star, that he thought they would hate him.

I am sure Anna wondered about why he never came back for her. I think he was ashamed of the killing of the Germans. He never told anyone about the Bronze Star Medal, not even his brothers and sisters. It wasn't until a magazine called the Stars and Stripes arrived at the farm telling the story of the battle of Appenrode Germany and told the role that Paul played in the battle and the story of the Bronze Star, that they knew any thing about it. But Paul never talked about it, or Anna. He never spoke a word about her, but I think he must have loved her very deeply. He kept her letters for 55 years.

Paul never married. He lived with his brother who also never married and his mother until her death in 1982. I know he probably thought about Anna, but realized she had forgotten about him after a while. Paul was a good man, kind spoken and would help anyone that he could. I think he just realized it was almost impossible that he and Anna could be together. I think in his heart, while he was in Germany, that he hoped he could bring her back to the United States, and that's why they were going to English lessons together.

I would just like Anna Reinoehl, if she is still alive to know that Paul must have loved her very much.

I have all four letters, and I would be glad to copy them and send a copy to the family if they would like to have them.

Enclosed are several pictures of Paul when he was in the Army and one is in Germany.

Write back if you would like, and I would love to have a picture of Anna when she was about 18 or so if possible, because I consider her to be the only love of Paul's life, and he was my uncle and I loved my Uncle very much.

Thank You,
Debbie King

17
Truth Will Stand When the World Falls Down

A few months passed and I didn't receive an answer to my letters. I kept hoping, but after about four months, I knew I would not hear from Anna or her relatives. Although I fantasized about what it would be like for her to receive this letter after all this time, waiting and wondering about Paul, and what it might mean to her. I could imagine Anna, an old woman now, sitting reading my letter—me telling her about this great love that Paul had had for her and suddenly after all these years, she knew that he had not forgotten her, that indeed he had loved her.

I was totally drawn into this love story, and wanted to know everything I could find out about Fahrenzhausen. I searched on the internet, but everything I found was in German and I could not read German.

I had no idea how to find Anna, if she was still alive. I had about given up when I talking to someone on the internet about this story and they suggested I put a post on a German website.

I had never thought about that. I had looked at all kinds of web-sites in German, but the idea had not really crossed my mind. It was a great idea, but in the back of my mind I doubted it would really be of any help. My fears of never finding Anna were so great, and I was so afraid that the story would die with me always wondering about Anna, and that I too, would grieve for Anna as Paul did, not knowing what became of her. The idea of Anna longing for Paul, as in 1946, and her never knowing that he loved her as much as she loved him, really disturbed me. I became so obsessed with the tale of the two lovers, that sometimes I would be on my way to work in my car, and would be thinking of this sad tale that I would just have to pull my car over and cry.

I decided to try the post on the German website, and I put my e-mail address on the bottom of the short message. I entitled it "World War II love story, gone wrong." If anything would get attention in Germany, maybe the title would. A month or so later I got an email from the webmaster of that website and he said that people had been trying to e-mail me, and that I had not responded to their e-mails. He said that at least I should respond, and thank them for the offer to help. I was dumfounded by this, because I had not received any e-mails from that post. I didn't even know what this person was saying. So, I apologized and explained to him that I had lots of posts on the internet relating to family history and that I always answered my posts as a gesture of friendship. I went back and looked at that post I had placed on the website, and I saw what the problem was. When I signed up on the website I had typed my e-mail address in correctly but what was posted on the actual site, I had accidentally left out one character in the address. That was why when they e-mailed me, I never received it.

I fixed the error and replied back to the webmaster that I had corrected the error and that I had made a notice of my mistake in my post.

Within a day or so I received an email from a lady who said she might be able to help me. Through days of correspondence with her, and me sending some information to her home in Frankfurt, Vera Nagel said she could help me. She found a website that listed all people's names and telephone numbers, like a telephone book. She looked at all the paper work I had sent her and sent me two addresses for someone in Fahrenzhausen who might be a relative of Anna.

The address she sent to me, was for Niklas Reinoehl, and when I looked back through Anna's letters, I recognized the name. I got really excited, because this had to be her brother. How could it not be?

That night I sat down and wrote a small letter to Mr. And Mrs. Niklas Reinoehl. I enclosed the original letter that I had written explaining the whole story.

My hopes were high as I mailed one letter to his work address, and the other to his home address in January of 2007.

I had actually started talking to Mary about writing to the Reinoehl family a couple of months before, and she would ask me occasionally if I had ever got any response from my letters. I would just say no, not yet, and this went on for awhile. But these new letters had a chance, I thought. If Niklas Reinoehl got them and decided to answer me, I would be thrilled. I figured he was pretty old by now, and he might not have a computer, but I put my e-mail address on the bottom of the letter anyway. If I received a response, I was sure it would come by mail.

Somewhere in Germany

A month went by and by this time David and I had really become curious about Fahrenzhausen. We downloaded a satellite imagery website tool, and started looking at Fahrenzhausen and Munich. Fahrenzhausen was still a small town and I couldn't imagine how small it was when Paul was there. It had just one hotel called the Ampevilla, and something that looked like a factory or greenhouse, and a lot of gardens and farmland around the little town. We found out it was about seventeen miles north of Munich, "München" they had called it in German.

We bought a travel book on Munich and read a lot about that city, but they did not mention Fahrenzhausen. There were lots of little towns and villages all around Munich, probably too many to mention them all. Fahrenzhausen was just a spot on the map as far as the travel book was concerned, not worth mentioning to prospective travelers. But I could see that it was a quaint and quiet little town, though I could not tell a lot from the satellite imagery. The travel book had a CD in the back of it, that taught you a little of the German language. I started listening to it in my car, thinking that someday we might go to Munich and Fahrenzhausen to see where Anna had lived, and where Paul was when the two of them fell in love. It would almost take my breath as I would think of being there in Fahrenzhausen, just because of that very reason. I could not imagine being there in that little town, standing there in the same spot where Paul had stood sixty years earlier. I wondered how the town had changed and if anyone there could possibly remember the American soldiers being there, standing post.

There still was no word in February from the Reinoehls. I knew it took about two weeks for the letters to get overseas. But

I thought by now I should be getting a response. I looked in the mailbox every day when I came home from work, but there was never anything from Germany.

I made Mary a scrapbook out of the color copies I had made of the sixty-year-old letters from Anna, and a copy of the interpretations and of Paul's war records. Anna's letters were so lovely and touching of her love for Paul, I kept wishing I had a picture of Anna. I didn't even know what she looked like, and I would have liked to have had a picture of her as well, to put in that scrapbook. Maybe there was a picture of her somewhere, but I had no idea.

I kept thinking of going back to the old garage for a further look to see if there was something I had missed there. If I found the letters there, could there possibly be something else that I had not found? I had tried to rack my brain about the contents of the boxes I carried back to Charles, but I felt reasonably certain that I had been pretty thorough in my search, and that I probably already had everything I needed to collect from those boxes. It was still cold outside anyway, so I decided I would just have to wait till warmer weather.

Friday, March 9th was just nine days short of my fifty-first birthday. I started out the morning just as I normally do, with the same routine that I always follow before going to work. Every morning I check my e-mail and this morning was no different. When I retrieved my e-mail, there was something from someone named Sofie. I had been getting a lot of those foreign lottery e-mails and was warned not to open them because of computer viruses. I almost deleted the e-mail, but something told me to see what it was about.

Somewhere in Germany

I got the shock of my life when I realized it was a response from someone who knew the Reinoehl family. As I read, I couldn't believe my eyes at what the content of this email was.

Dear Miss King,

First let me introduce myself. My name is Sofie. I live in Munich. I am 31 years old, and someone asked me translate a letter to you. The name of this person is Josiah Reinoehl, and he is the second husband of my mother. I hope that my translation wouldn't include too much mistakes.

Here is Josiah's letter:

Dear Miss King,

My name is Josiah Reinoehl and I got your letter on some roundabout ways. In this letter you wrote about the big love between Anna Reinoehl and Paul. You also asked about a picture from Anna, but this will be difficult, because she is very ill now and I don't know what will happened to her if I would ask her to give me a picture for this reason.

Five years ago, she had a stroke and I am not sure what she is remembering for.

I have attached two pictures but the quality is not very good. The first picture shows Anna when she was married 50 years ago. The second picture shows me, Josiah Reinoehl.

I was born on May 7th, 1946. Probably I am the result of this big love. For that reason, I want to know, why he never send any sign of life.

You wrote that maybe he was ashamed of killing Germans, but at that time, there was war, and if he didn't, maybe he had being killed by Germans and he never could come back at home.

I would be very lucky if you could send me a picture from Paul, because I was waiting for 61 years to see him.

I hope I meet your expectations, and you will write back to the following address:

> *Josiah Reinoehl*
> *Gartier 17*
> *85777 Fahrenzhausen*
> *Germany*

I couldn't believe my eyes at what I was reading. Did I just read what I thought I read—"probably I am the result of this big love?" I read and read the letter over and over again. I ran my hands through my hair. "Oh my God, Paul has a son!!!!" I remember saying to myself.

I had waited so long to hear from the Reinoehls, wanted to know what had happened to Anna, to know if she was still living or had died. But I never never never expected to hear that Paul could possibly have a son!

I was shocked. I was so shocked that I ran into the kitchen, I was having a hard time breathing because when something of this magnitude hits you, it can knock the breath right out of you.

I called David and told him that I had heard from the Reinoehls, and that Paul had a son. I don't even remember what else I said to him. I just couldn't believe it. David was as shocked as I was.

Somewhere in Germany

I printed out the e-mail and it had a picture of Anna when she was around seventy or so. Josiah's picture was probably when he was about thirty-five. Josiah was sixty years old, soon to be sixty-one. I went off to work but the e-mail stayed on my mind all day. I couldn't even function well at work, because I was still so shocked. Josiah never left my thoughts all day.

I had wanted so badly to reach Anna in Fahrenzhausen, but now I knew the answer to some of my questions. Anna was still alive! She had to be seventy-eight or seventy-nine years old. She had had a stroke. Now I doubted Anna would ever know how much Paul loved her, because of her condition. Her son—Paul and Anna's son!—could never say he had heard news about his father, because the news might cause her to have another stroke.

On Friday evening when the shock was still evident, I e-mailed Vera Nagel to let her know that I had received a letter from the Reinoehl Family. It was just a short note and attached was Sofie's letter and the letter from Josiah.

Dear Vera:

You are not going to believe this!!!!!!! What a shocker I got this morning from Germany from the Reinoehl family. Read the attached message.

Debbie King

Here is Vera Nagel's response to my letter about the Reinoehls:

Debbie,

I am sitting here reading the letter from Josiah again and again, and like you, I can't believe what I am reading.

As you said, "It's shocking and wonderful." So Josiah is Anna's and Paul's son. The child from the "Big love of Anna and Paul."

In all of her letters she never mentioned by just a single word or any other covering wording that she was pregnant or so. Josiah gives his birthdate as May 7, 1946. So when Anna wrote the letters to Paul—the four letters from 1946 to 1948—she had given birth to her son. Maybe I am way too excited at this moment (so I don't seem to be able to figure it out myself) but do you know for sure when Paul left Fahrenzhausen? Obviously knowing nothing about Anna's pregnancy?

So do we have to interpret her letters to him as a cry for help?

The only possible explanation I am able to think about at this moment may be that she was deeply ashamed of having an illegitimate son of an American soldier and didn't want to mention this in her letters because she didn't want Paul to reply just because of this fact. Or may be because she knew that all the letters were being censored, and was afraid that if she had included this to Paul that Paul would have never gotten any of her letters. I don't know but it's very tragic.

Not long ago, I watched a reportage at German television dealing with the faith of illegitimate "War children" and how hard the life of the mothers an theirs as well often was. Often those children were taken away from their mothers and put into a farm for babies and young. So Josiah's own story may be tragic too.

And when I read the translation of this letter provided by this step-daughter, Sofie…saying "I hope I meet your expectations"….I find these words very touching although it may be also a translation issue. He definitely had absolutely no need to be excused for anything or to "meet anybody's expectations," right? And if he really used this phrase in his original German letter then I would think those show a very deep inner feeling of a child, and now a man born into society which segregated them and handled them in a non acceptable way—to say it polite.

What do you think of all this? What are your feelings? What would you like to do now? Just a personal thought: be careful to reply to his step-daughter since he wants you to reply directly to him!

Vera Nagel
Frankfurt, Germany

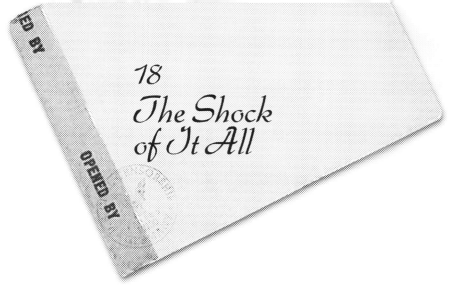

18
The Shock
of It All

*W*hen Josiah received my letter, it was through his Uncle Niklas. That's why he said he got my letter in a round-about way. Josiah's birthday is May 7th, 1946. When you think about his birthdate you would have thought that Paul would have known Anna was pregnant since he left London in May just approximately two weeks after Josiah was born. First, you have to remember that Paul left Fahrenzhausen around January, just before Anna realized she was pregnant. She did not know how to contact him there in London and he did not know she was pregnant before he left Fahrenzhausen, or before he got on the ship there in London. After she did not hear from him, she thought he either went back to the United States or had been killed.

For sixty-one years Josiah had never known anything about his father, except what his mother or his grandparents had told him. Understandably, he was bitter. In his first letter he said "I want to know why he never sent any sign of life." Although he was bitter, he said he felt "very lucky" (happy) if we would send pictures of his father.

It was Sofie, his stepdaughter who contacted us and translated for Josiah. Sofie speaks and writes and reads English and Josiah cannot. He only speaks German. Sofie lives in Munich.

I had time to think about Josiah, and the shocking truth of it all, after receiving his letter. Paul's son, I had to keep reminding myself, was not just a stranger but Paul's son. Paul had been dead since 2001, and the regrets of not knowing this sooner began to pile up.

Josiah would never get to know his father, as we did, but I was certain that he was Paul's son. The dates of Paul's military service, and while he was in Fahrenzhausen, and the desperate tone of Anna's letters convinced me that he had to be Paul's son. His picture even favors our family.

I have to say that in the days after hearing this news, I was a nervous wreck. I had found out something, quite by accident that could enormously affect our entire family and make them change the way they thought of someone who they knew their entire lives. How in the world could I tell them about Josiah, Paul's son? The sound of it sounded so unreal, would they believe it to be the truth?

It was Josiah's right to know everything about Paul for he had been denied it for so long now. So later that day, I e-mailed him pictures and said that I would be sending a package with lots of information about his father as soon as possible.

Telling Mary and Charles about their nephew was going to be hard. We didn't know how they would take it. Mary was seventy-seven; Charles was seventy-nine. What if we caused them to have a heart attack? I was so scared that they would be mad at me for digging into someone else's business and putting my nose into somewhere it didn't belong. But when we told them, it was David who put it best. He said that it didn't matter what they thought about it, because "the Truth will stand when the world falls down." How true it was. After all these years, the truth has finally come out. Now Charles and Mary knew just how much Anna and Paul had been in love.

When we told Mary, she was at home, and we took her outside and told her that we had heard from the Reinoehls. She wanted to know what they said. David told her that Paul had a son, and that his name was Josiah, and we showed her the e-mail. She sat there shocked for a moment, and then we decided to get her to go with us to tell Charles, because we were not sure how he would react.

When we went to Charles, and Mary had went with us. She acted like a little kid, running around and showing the picture ooopsf Josiah, while David tried to explain about the old letters, and about the recent e-mail we had received. Charles just smiled at the news and seemed happy that something of Paul had gone on, that he had left something in this world.

I told them that something spiritual had driven me to find the letters in the garage, and to try to find Anna. Maybe Paul, who had gone to heaven and knew the truth, had led me to find Josiah.

Charles had known about the letters received at the farmhouse years ago, but he hadn't known that Paul and Anna had been in love. He said that Paul had kept them in one of Adell's old hatboxes in his bedroom all those years. He said that Paul had talked about going back to Germany, until about five years after he had returned from the war; after that he didn't talk about it anymore, that he had given up on the hope of going back there. But he carried a picture of Anna in his wallet until it was worn completely in two.

Later we found a picture of Anna, Paul had stuck it in an old photo album and nobody knew who she was, except for Paul. The picture had been forgotten about by everyone but him. It was an exact picture of the one he carried in his wallet until it was worn out, and the only way we knew it was Anna, was that it had a faint stamp on the back that we made out part of it with a strong magnifying glass. I took it to a jeweler who verified what it said on the back.

Upon learning of Josiah's existence, and feeling bad and sad, for Anna and realizing not only had she had to endure a pregnancy alone and confused, I also did some research on the internet on what the women had to go through who gave birth to the children of American Soldiers during World War II.

As of 1955, up to 67,700 German children had been fathered by U.S. soldiers. Here are the difficult facts of their lives:

1) The women and children were shamed in their communities, called names; some of the pregnant women had to endure their heads being shaved for proving their consorting with the enemy by getting pregnant by an American G.I.

2) If the German government found out that the baby belonged to an American soldier, some were taken from their homes and put into orphanages, to grow up there.

3) The German women who were pregnant, were warned in newspapers by the American Government that they had no legal rights for assistance from the American Government and that if the soldier in question had gone back to the United States, his address would not be divulged to the German woman.

4) If a soldier was suspected of having had a sexual relationship with a German fraulein, he would be immediately transferred and the whereabouts of his transfer would be kept strictly confidential.

All this information, I got off the internet about what Anna had to go through and what Josiah must have had to go through when he was just a child, made me feel even worse for the both of them. I felt so sorry.

19
The Family Comes Full Circle

*A*s time went by, we received e-mails from Josiah and his wife Lena, Sofie's mother. Sofie had to translate and it would take time from us e-mailing, her translating and then getting the letter to Josiah. Josiah would write, take it to Sofie in Munich, and then Sofie has to translate, and then email it to us. So it's like a circle. The family circle.

As far as we are all concerned we and Josiah and his family are just that. We are all family. Josiah and Lena has Sofie and a son who live next to Josiah and Lena.

Anna waited five years for Paul to return to Fahrenzhausen. In 1951 she married a Hungarian refugee that had come to Fahrenzhausen in 1946. They are still married today and she lives with him near Josiah and Lena, and Niklas. She had the stroke about five years previously, about the same time that Paul had died, and sometimes they say she is like a child, and cries like a baby, and other times she is like her old self, but you never know from one day to the next.

Somewhere in Germany

I wondered since Anna wrote to Paul in 1946, after Josiah was born in May, why she didn't tell him that she had had their child. In all four letters she never mentioned that she had had their baby. I used to think that she wanted Paul to want her for her, and not for the baby. But then I learned a lot about censorship. There was a Civil Censorship Service that censored the letters during and after the war. If a soldier wrote something when writing to home that he was not supposed to tell, then it would be blacked out. If it was serious enough, it would not be sent through. If a woman who had a child of an American soldier wrote and told him about the baby, it would probably either be sent back to her, or just not be allowed to be sent period. So I think that was why she did not tell him about Josiah, their son. Sofie told us that Anna did try to write a Paul a letter in 1948 along with a picture of her and Josiah together. The letter came back and had been opened, and the picture was no longer inside. Someone had removed the picture and sent the letter back to Anna. This may have been a job done by the censorship.

Josiah has told us a little about his life in Fahrenzhausen. He had lived there most of his life and he said that when he was a child, he had a hard time growing up as an occupational child, because he did not know his father, and most of the townspeople knew his father was American. He said that he swore that he would show them all and be successful. He said that he had a wonderful childhood due to the fact that he grew up in the Garden district and still lives there today. He is proud that his father was an American soldier.

I find it ironic, that when Paul was there standing post in Fahrenzhausen that little Sonya and Niklas would go and sit with him. Paul would give them candies and fruit, things that they could not get. When Josiah was a young boy, he went and sat with The American soldiers who still stood post near Fahrenzhausen, the same post that Paul was at, and they gave him candies and fruits, and cigarettes which he carried to his grandfather and his uncle Niklas, and he said that made them very happy.

Josiah joined the German Air Force and was there in 1968, and 1969. When he was about thirty, he found out where his father lived, I guess from Anna, and he started taking English lessons, planning to come to America to visit him. But he thought that if Paul had gotten married, his visit might ruin Paul's life, and so Josiah changed his mind, and forgot all about coming to the U.S., and the English lessons.

One thing I find interesting is that some of the older people of Fahrenzhausen think of Paul as a legend; they still talk to Josiah about his father. They remember when Paul was there, because they told Josiah that just after the War, when all the refugees came through, that Paul was instrumental in helping the German people of Fahrenzhausen keep their livestock, and their animals such as cows, horses, and "porks" (pigs). And most of the older people remember him with kindness.

I have to say that I smile when I think about something that Sofie told me in her email later after we had gotten to know them a bit. She said that in Fahrenzhausen, Germany, that in the middle of Josiah's garden stands a flag pole, and there an American flag flies proudly. He evidently is now proud of his American heritage.

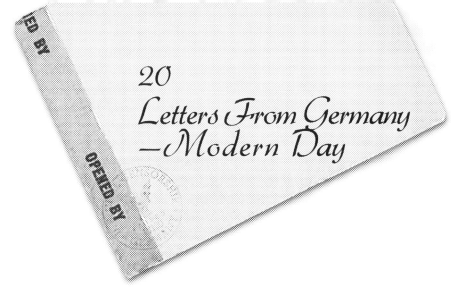

20
Letters From Germany
—Modern Day

Letter from Sofie, dated March 18, 2007:

Dear Debbie,

Sometimes my mum told me little stories about Josiah. One time she told me that Anna sent a letter with pictures from herself and Josiah as a baby to Paul. The letter came back, but without the pictures. So Josiah never knew if Paul received the pictures or not. I remember that some years ago Josiah found out where Paul is living, and he took some English lessons but not much. First he planned to visit Paul, but then he felt unsure. He imagined that Paul had family and he was afraid that he will destroy the family. So he stopped taking further lessons. At this time I did not no why because he is also a very quite man who is not talking too much, you know. Maybe it will take some time until he will answer, but I will forward all answers asap.

Greetings
Sofie

Somewhere in Germany

Letter from me, dated March 21, 2007:

Hallo Sofie,

Tell Josiah that I sent a package yesterday with better pictures of Paul and some of his military papers that you or someone may have to translate for him. I wanted him to get a sense of our family, so I have sent pictures of my family, Charles, and Mary and Josiah's grandmother by Paul. I also sent a map of the southern area of The United States, so that Josiah will get a sense of the region that we live in. I have pinpointed out the area, and sent some brochures of the area we are in. In this package are color copies of the original letters that Anna sent Paul in 1946 and 1948. He will know what they say when he gets them, for he will be able to read them for himself. Look at the dates on these letters.

Also, I want to tell you something about censorship. The United States government censored all the letters coming from Germany for a long time, because of the war. If there was anything they didn't want divulged in the letters, they would either black out the lettering, or send the letter back. I wonder sometimes if they did not want these soldiers to find out they had fathered children with German women. Anna's letters passed through the censorship but I fear that the one that was sent with the picture of Anna and the baby (Josiah) was returned and the picture was taken out. Why, I am not sure, but if Anna sent it and Paul never received it, and it was eventually returned back to Anna without the picture, then something must have happened in between. I believe this could have been done by the censorship.

We would feel very lucky to hear from Josiah soon. I know he is thinking of everything, and it is a lot to think about, but Mary and Charles keep asking me if I heard from him.

Of course, you are my link to Josiah and I welcome anything you have to say to us about Josiah and what happened to him in his childhood. I am so very sad that the story happened the way it did.

Nothing more for now.

Please urge Josiah to think about writing soon.

Debbie

Letter from Sofie, Munich, dated March 26, 2007:

Hi Debbie,

You do not make a mistake. Like you said, Josiah had a lot to think about, and first he did not know how to start. I talked to my mother that she should ask him how he is feeling, and what he is thinking about. That was the right way for him and he gave me a letter for you today.

I only have to translate it when my children will be sleeping this evening. Some of your questions will be answered and there will be a lot more questions.

Try to be patient.

I hope you had a nice weekend.

Greetings,

Sofie

Somewhere in Germany

Letter from Sofie, translating for Josiah, dated March 28th, 2007:

Hi Debbie,

Today I will send you Josiah's letter. It is not much, but it's the beginning. I guess there will be more with each letter.

Dear Debbie,

Today I would like to tell you a little bit about me. I was born on May 7th in 1946. The first years of my life I lived with my mother and grandparents, and their son Niklas. Niklas is my uncle. I had a great time there, but there were a few people who were very malicious because my father was an American soldier and I did not know him. But I was always proud of having an American as father, and for this reason I always tried to be near the American soldiers which were still here. They often give me chocolate, oranges, bananas, and things we usually could not bought at this time. Anna, my mother married in 1951 to a refugee. He came here in 1946.

My mother did not told me much about my father. Even though I was very interested of course. Although I grew up without my father, I have reached every thing I wanted to do. I have a son. I visited school from 1952 to 1960. I made my education as a clerk from 1960 in Munich to 1963, later I started working for another company. I work there still as a manager. From 1968 to 1969 I was in the German Air force. Later in life I married Lena, my wife.

Dear relatives, I hope I could answer some of your questions. I will write soon.
Sincerely,
Josiah Reinoehl

Letter from Lena and Josiah, dated April 20th, 2007:

Dear relatives,

Today I (Lena) will start with this letter something about me. I was very lucky when my husband told me that he had heard something from his father. His Uncle Niklas gave him the letter you sent and he said to Josiah that his father was dying, but he did not understand English. When I first met Josiah in 1978, one of the first things he told me was that his father was an American soldier.

I was born in Uruguay in 1948, but my parents were both German who had left Germany and came there because of the war. We came back to Germany in 1965. We are very informal people like you. Josiah helped me a lot as long as I know him, and I liked him very much all the time. But it took us along time to stay together, so we married late. But now I feel very lucky.

Easter Sunday, we visited Anna. She is very ill now. So we have not the heart to tell her the news from you. We do not know what this means for her health. But we know that she loved Paul very much.

From Josiah:

This was some information about my wife's life and the beginning of our love. Some of elder people in Fahrenzhausen remembered Paul and sometimes they talk with me about him. They knew him as a very kindly and helpful man. When the poles leaved Germany after the war they wanted to take the last things from the people here, and

Paul helped them to kept their belongings and animals and horses, and porks and cows.

For me, it was not easy to handle the teasings at school because I was an occupational child. I vowed then that I would show them and become successful. I now have everything I need, and no one says anything to me about being an occupational child anymore.

The Americans were here when I was a child. They gave me treats when I would sit with them as they stood post. They gave me cigarettes which I gave to my grandfather and uncle , and they were very thankful for that.
I will close for now, the work in the gardens is beginning, and I will be busy for a while. I will write soon.
Josiah Reinoehl

Letter from Sofie, dated May 15, 2007:

Hi Debbie,

I hope you are feeling better, as you said you were having trouble with your stomach.

I want to explain something about the mentalities of the people in the time after the war. Maybe it can explain some things to you.

When a woman got pregnant it was the "default" of the woman. I can remember when I was about 14 years old a woman in our village got pregnant and the older people said it was her own "default." It was very hard for them to find a husband. And they need a husband because it was very difficult to find work as women. A woman has to stay at home with the children and they have not many rights. Thank God it has changed!

The women did a lot of work until the soldiers come back home from war or bondage, and the women at this time were called *Truemmerfrauen* (I found the word, rubble women) because they were building up the towns which were sometimes completely destroyed in the war. When their husbands came back, they have to stay at home again.

A rule here is that children don't have to know everything, and that is probably why Anna never told Josiah much about his father. Josiah looked at Niklas like his father, even though he was his uncle, but its Josiah turn to tell you more about his life.

Anna lives in a town above Josiah, It is very difficult to talk to her because of her illness.

Greetings to everyone,

Sofie

Letter from Sofie. Dated June 18th 2007

Hi Debbie,

I was surprised when Josiah and my mother Lena told me that they were thinking of visiting you in American maybe next year. I never thought that Josiah would ever want to travel so far. Josiah and Lena start Englisch lessons soon.

The last week I went to see Josiah and Lena several times, for the cherries came in. I love to make marmalade and forgot how much work it is. But I love cherries. We have strawberry fields too, and we go and pick the strawberries and take cream with us and we have strawberries and cream in the fields. I take my children with me and they love the cream and strawberries in the field.

Greetings,

Sofie

Letter from Josiah and Lena, dated June 20, 2007:

Today, we received the package you sent with pictures on which we can see part of Paul's life. I guess it's a nice area to live. I will put in an album, where we will collect all the information and the pictures you have sent and will send to us.

Josiah's and my birthday are both in May, and time passes by very fast. Here in Germany we do not visit very often but on such days, such as birthdays, everyone tries to come, I feel sorry you are living so far away.

You know my daughter Sofie. When we received the first letter from you, we asked Sofie to translate it and she agreed immediately. So this is very comfortable for us while we could not read or write English, and in Josiah's case it is not enough to communicate.

I want to tell you about Anna. I am very sad we could not tell her all the news and stories from you. She loves Josiah very much and she is very lucky when she see's him. But she also cries a lot. The illness destroyed a part of her brain, so she could not speak clearly and she forgets a lot. She talks about her parents often, but sometimes we do not know what she is meaning. Her husband takes very good care of her so she is as well as she can be.

Josiah's part:

Thank you a lot for the birthday cards, congratulations, and pictures you sent me. I was very lucky to find out that there are so many relatives on my father's side. And now I know where my father's grave is and what it looks like. I thank you so much for that. In this moment, I am very busy. I have a lot to do in several associations, but this will become better soon. I will write more then.

Best regards,

Lena and Josiah

Letter from Sofie, dated July 27, 2007

Hi Debbie,

We are all doing fine now, but the last four weeks every member of our family except me was ill. But not all at the same time, I think you know this, when one feels better then another one gets started with the fever. So I need new batteries for myself. But now we are all fine.

I am sometimes dreaming of you all too. We haven't seen each other but we are dreaming of each other, isn't it funny?

In your last email you wrote about okra. I have tried one, but it tastes like nothing. How does okra usually tastes? And how do you use them. And you wrote about marmalade, "freezer jam" you called it. Can you send me the recipe?

Whenever you come to Germany, you and your family will be welcome. Last time I read an article about a man who was exactly in Josiah's situation. He found the address of his father in the U.S.A. There must be organizations that help German people with American fathers to get the address. Because of this father was very old, the organization gave him the address of the son.

The son wrote back and said that he shouldn't write back again. So this story shows me how lucky we could be that you are the family of Josiah, because you really accept him like he is.

My baby is now one year. George my oldest will start learning English at school in the next grade. And my middle child starts his why-time. Today is the last day for school and for the second grade he gets his certificate. Then he will have six weeks summer vacation.

I have to stop now, but I will write soon.
Greetings to everyone,
Sofie and familie

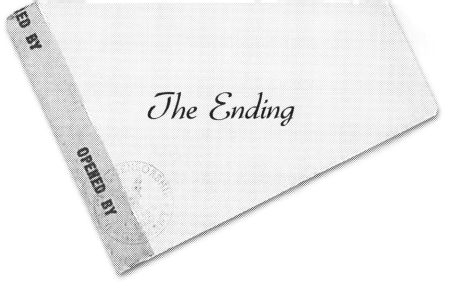

The Ending

*W*hen I was writing this book,
I visited Paul's grave…

One day when Charles and I went there
I asked him in a whisper to give me
Inspiration if he wanted this story told.

So I have decided, that some day, when all this is over,
I am going to take that little wooden box,
and I am going put the letters from Anna
and pictures of Josiah
and then I am going to dig a hole
at the foot of Paul's grave
and I am going to bury that
little wooden box, so that their spirits
can all be together
as they should have been in real life.